Revision for Maths

LEVELS 3–8
KEY STAGE 3 and GCSE

with answers

C.J. COX

JOHN MURRAY

Acknowledgements

The author would like to thank the following who have helped in the preparation of this book:
Peter Bland, his wife and Set 10/1 of Huish Episcopi School (especially David Screen).

First published in 1995
by John Murray (Publishers) Ltd
50 Albemarle Street, London W1X 4BD

Reprinted 1995, 1996 (twice), 1997

Typeset by AFS Image Setters Ltd, Glasgow
Illustrations by Hugh Neill
Printed in Great Britain by St Edmundsbury Press Ltd, Bury St Edmunds, Suffolk

A catalogue entry for this title can be obtained from the British Library

ISBN 0 7195 7083 2

CONTENTS

The following listing indicates the lowest National Curriculum (1995) level for each topic. If the level indicated is above the highest level of your tier of entry you need not revise that topic.

Number

USING THIS BOOK

This is a revision book for Levels 3 to 8 of the National Curriculum. It can be used for Key Stage 3 and Foundation and Intermediate Level GCSE.

If you are not taking the highest level papers, find out which notes you do not need to know. Beside each topic in the Contents is an indication of its minimum level, so a topic coded 8 need not be revised if your entry is at level 7 or lower.

The book is divided into five major sections: Number, Algebra, Shape, Measure and Data handling.

Each section is divided into headed topics, containing:

- notes
  These briefly explain the topic and should be read several times until you are sure you understand them.
- worked examples
  These will be of most value if you don't just read them, but copy them out and work through them yourself.
- do's and don'ts
  These warn you of mistakes that the author has seen time and time and time again in his 30 years of marking pupils' work. You could highlight the ones that you know apply specially to you!
- questions
  These have been carefully selected to help you check that you have understood the topic. Tick the boxes ✓ when you have completed the topic and have answered all the questions correctly.

There is usually enough space for your working and answers, but you will also need a few sheets of graph paper and some plain paper for large diagrams.

The glossary gives the meanings of words you might meet in questions, but which are not explained in the main part of this book. The index gives you page references where topics and meanings may be found.

You can use the book in two ways:

To revise every topic, work through from the beginning. It is important to practise answering the questions until you can answer them without difficulty, even if you have to do them several times. It is a good idea to return to them again after a few weeks to see if you can still do them.

To help you find out about any one particular topic, use the index to find out which pages to read.

Finally . . . this book is not magic. It does not work if you put it on a shelf or under your bed! You must use it, preferably little and often to avoid losing concentration, then you will gain your best possible result. Your teachers and the author of this book have done their best . . . now it is up to you.

HOW TO REVISE

- Start well before the date of the exam. Cramming at the last minute will muddle you.

- Find out what you need to know by looking at the **syllabus**. Ask your teacher or the examination board. Plan your campaign – draw up a timetable of what you need to revise and when you plan to do it. Don't be too ambitious; set yourself targets you can reach, otherwise you will give up. If you cannot face more than ten minutes a day then plan for that – it is better than nothing. Put your timetable where you will see it every day . . . and keep to it!

- Work through past papers. They show you the kind of questions you will be asked. Make a written note of topics you do not fully understand and revise them. You can look them up in this book. Practise each box until you get 100%. Then try again a few weeks later! Time yourself to make sure you learn to pace your work; rushing leads to silly mistakes; going too slowly causes panic.

- Revise in a quiet place. You might find background music helpful, but there must be nothing to distract your thoughts.

- Revise little and often. Most people start to lose concentration after about 20 minutes, so have a ten-minute break (but don't get hooked on something else like TV or a computer game!) then start again.

- Do not revise just once. Keep going back to a topic until you know it perfectly.

- It can help to work with a friend, teaching each other about topics, even if you know them already! Teaching someone else is the best way to teach yourself, and to make sure you really understand.

- Remember: Start early. Plan thoroughly. Stick to your plan.

TAKING EXAMS

Before the exam

- Ease off the revision a few days before the exam. Most people do not have the confidence to stop entirely in the last few days, though this is probably the best, but you will do badly if you go into the exam room tired and overstressed.
- Make sure you have everything you need – a reliable calculator, drawing instruments, etc. Do not buy things at the last minute – you need to get used to them; even rulers can be marked in different ways. Treat yourself to a pen that feels good to write with and use it a few times to get used to it.
- Arrive in time, but not too early. Deep, slow breathing helps control your nerves and sends lots of oxygen to your brain.

During the exam

- Keep calm! In mathematics papers the easiest questions often come first, but if a later question looks easier to you, start with that one. Once you have answered one question your confidence will grow. Leave difficult questions until the end when it will not matter so much if your brain does get into a panic.
- Pace yourself! Keep an eye on the time. It is boring to finish early, but dangerous to rush at the end. A steady pace is best.
- Read all through a question before you start to answer it.
- If someone else in the room annoys you, tell a supervisor – even if it is the supervisor's squeaky shoes!
- This flow chart contains good advice. Follow it!

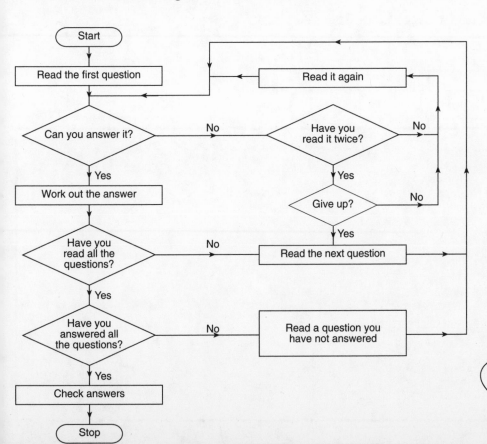

Use the glossary (page 104) for words you do not understand.

N1 ● THE DENARY NUMBER SYSTEM FOR INTEGERS

A denarius was a Roman coin divided into 10 asses.

Column headings

• The denary system uses ten digits (0 to 9) placed in columns.
A figure in one column stands for ten times as much as the same figure in the column on its right.

A million is a thousand thousand.

millions	hundred-thousands	ten-thousands	thousands	hundreds	tens	ones
1 000 000s	100 000s	10 000s	1000s	100s	10s	1s
10^6	10^5	10^4	10^3	10^2	10^1	10^0

Writing numbers

Example:

2001   two thousand and one

18 046   eighteen thousand and forty-six

80 010 000   eighty million, ten thousand

The **ones** column is often called the **units** column.

Example:
4125 is 4 thousands, 1 hundred, 2 tens and 5 ones.

10^6 means
$10 \times 10 \times 10 \times 10 \times 10 \times 10$.

DON'T	spell forty wrongly, for example as 'fourty'.
DO	write down correct spellings of words you often spell wrongly and keep testing yourself.

DON'T	start the millions too soon.
DO	remember to group in threes.

Note the digits are put into groups of three in large numbers.

A

1 Write these numbers in words.
  a 8105 _____
  b 50 003 _____
  c 300 500 000 _____

2 Write these numbers in figures.
  a two thousand and twenty _____
  b $56\frac{1}{2}$ million _____

3 Arrange these numbers in order of size, from smallest to largest.
  306   89   890   984   1001   55   66   9

  _____

N2 ● THE DENARY NUMBER SYSTEM FOR FRACTIONS

Extending the column system

• The column system is continued as in this chart.

hundreds	tens	ones • tenths	hundredths	thousandths
100s	10s	1s · $\frac{1}{10}$s	$\frac{1}{100}$s	$\frac{1}{1000}$s
10^2	10^1	10^0 · 10^{-1}	10^{-2}	10^{-3}

To show where the ones end and the tenths start, a dot called the **decimal point** is written between the figures. It is best written halfway up the figures, like 3·5, but in print it is often placed like a full stop.
• The figures after the decimal point should be said separately unless the number is an amount of money.

In some countries a comma is used instead of a dot.

Examples:

£1.36 is read 'One pound thirty six' *but* . . . 1.36 m is 'One point three six metres'.

90.08 is read 'ninety point zero eight', or 'ninety point nought eight'.

0.76 is read 'zero point seven six', or 'nought point seven six', or just 'point seven six'.

DON'T write .76; it is far too easy to miss the point and see it as seventy-six.

Example:
Write these numbers in order of size, from largest to smallest.

0.003	0.98	1.45	0.01	10	0	0.104	0.014

Answer: 10   1.45   0.98   0.104   0.014   0.01   0.003   0

DON'T read decimals like 0.38 (nought point three eight) as 'nought point thirty-eight'.

DO remember that only money can be read that way.

DON'T think that a decimal like 1.238 is larger than 1.25 because it has more figures.

DO remember place value. The five hundredths makes 1.25 bigger than 1.238 (which has only three hundredths), whatever comes further to the right.

Multiplying and dividing by 10, 100, 1000, etc.

• When you multiply a number by ten its digits move one column **to the left** so they become worth ten times as much.
• When you divide a number by ten its digits move one column **to the right** so they become worth a tenth as much.

You can also think of this as moving the decimal point.

Examples:

To multiply or divide by 100, move two columns.

To multiply or divide by 1000, move three columns.

Examples:

	1000s	100s	10s	1s $\cdot$	$\frac{1}{10}$s	$\frac{1}{100}$s	$\frac{1}{1000}$s
3.57				3 $\cdot$ 5	7		
3.57 × 10			3	5 $\cdot$ 7			
3.57 × 100		3	5	7 $\cdot$			
3.57 × 1000	3	5	7	0 $\cdot$			

	1000s	100s	10s	1s $\cdot$	$\frac{1}{10}$s	$\frac{1}{100}$s	$\frac{1}{1000}$s
49			4	9 $\cdot$			
49 ÷ 10				4 $\cdot$ 9			
49 ÷ 100				0 $\cdot$ 4	9		
49 ÷ 1000				0 $\cdot$ 0	4	9	

The zero in 3570 is needed to show the empty units column.

The first zeros in 0.49 and 0.049 are needed to make sure the decimal point is seen.

The second zero in 0.049 is needed to show the empty tenths column.

DON'T move the wrong way.

DO remember: **Multiplying makes bigger.**
Dividing makes smaller.

Note: The rule above is only for integer multiplication.
If you **multiply** by a **fraction** the answer is **smaller**.
If you **divide** by a **fraction** the answer is **bigger**.

A

1 Write these numbers in words.
  a 16.035 _____
  b 1000.001 _____

2 State the value of the figure 7 in each of these numbers.
  a 170.5 _____
  b 1.07 _____
  c 13.1576 _____

3 Write these in order of size, largest first.
  3.5   3.55   3.25   3.059   3   3.08   3.9   3.901

  _____

4 Comment on the answer when a calculator is used to work out £3.45—£1.95.

  _____
  _____

5 a 85 × 100   **b** 6.5 × 1000   **c** 0.52 × 100

  _____   _____   _____

6 a 97 ÷ 10   **b** 4.6 ÷ 10   **c** 15.82 ÷ 1000

  _____   _____   _____

7 How many times bigger is 1000 than 0.001? _____

8 Explain how questions **5** to **7** can be answered 'in your head'.

  _____
  _____

'In your head' means working out the answer without writing anything down.

N3 ● THE FOUR RULES WITHOUT A CALCULATOR

Learning
- Know the addition bonds from $1+1$ to $9+9$.
- Know the multiplication bonds from 1×1 to 9×9.
  Learn them in the order: 2s, 3s, 5s, 4s, 8s, 6s, 9s, 7s.

DO	learn the number bonds (add and multiply for any two digits). Write them on flash cards (e.g. 9×7 on one side, 63 on the other) and practise.

When you reach the 7s the only bond you have to learn is 7×7.

Your teacher can show you the 9 times 'on your hands'.

Setting out
- To show that you did not use a calculator, show carried figures.

Examples:

Sum
```
    8 0 6
  + 3 9 7
  -------
  1 2 0 3
      1 1
```

Difference
```
  ⁷8̸ ⁹0̸ ¹6
  -  3 9 7
  --------
     4 0 9
```

Product
```
      3 6 7
  ×     7 8
  ---------
    2 9 3 6
      5 5
  2 5 6 9 0
    4 4
  ---------
  2 8 6 2 6
      1 1
```

Quotient
```
        3 2
  23)7 3 ⁴6
```

DON'T	subtract 'upside-down', especially when the top number is zero.
DO	remember, 'Top take away bottom'.

DON'T	omit the zero in the second line of a multiplication.
DO	remember you are multiplying by a ten, and any whole number multiplied by ten ends in nought.

DON'T	divide the wrong way round, especially when the divisor is larger than the dividend, e.g. $16 \div 32$.
DO	write the first number (16), then draw the 'bus shelter' and put the second number (32) in front.

The divisor divides into the dividend to give the quotient.

DO	think, 'Is my answer sensible?'

DON'T	omit a zero part-way through a division. The answer to $404 \div 2$ is 202, *not* 22.
DO	remember that empty columns must contain a zero.

A

Show your full working. Do not use a calculator.

1 a $36.7 + 8$ _____

b $7.9 - 5.98$ _____

c $4005 - 1348$ _____

d $20.56 - 13.387$ _____

2 a 357×46 _____

b $172 \div 2$ _____

c $721 \div 7$ _____

N4 ● MENTAL CALCULATION

Addition
- Learn your addition bonds up to $9+9$, so that you can recall them instantly.
- When the numbers are small, look for pairings that make 10.

Example:

$5+3+4+\underbrace{7+3}+\underbrace{2+7}+8+9$

Answer: $8 + 4 + 10 + 10 + 7 + 9 = 48$

- With large numbers, add the largest value digits first.

Example:

$145 + 58 + 398 + 304 + 19$

Add the hundreds: $100 + 300 + 300 = 700$

Add the tens: $40 + 50 + 90 + 10 = 190$, making 890 so far.

Add on the units: $890 + 5 + 8 + 8 + 4 + 9 = 924$

Answer: $145 + 58 + 398 + 304 + 19 = 924$

Subtraction
- **Either**: Try to find an easy subtraction, then adjust the answer.

Example:

Work out $78 - 39$.

 $78 - 38 = 40$ which is taking away one too few,
so $78 - 39 = 39$.

Answer: $78 - 39 = 39$

- **Or:** Use adding on, like giving change in a shop.

Example:

Work out $145 - 58$.

58 to 60 is 2

60 to 145 is 85

58 to 145 is $85 + 2 = 87$

Answer: $145 - 58 = 87$

Multiplication
- You must know your tables (see the hints in Section N3).
- For numbers above 10 break them down into parts.

Example:

Work out 56×45.

$(50 \times 40) + (50 \times 5) \qquad + (6 \times 40) \qquad + (6 \times 5)$

$2000 \; + \; 250 \to 2250 + \; 240 \to 2490 + \; 30 \to 2520$

Answer: $56 \times 45 = 2520$

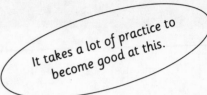

It takes a lot of practice to become good at this.

Division

- You cannot divide if you do not know your tables.
- You need to imagine the normal working written out, but you can write the answer as you go.

A

1 Work these out in your head.

   a $67 + 134 + 36 + 70$ _____   **b** $45 + 51 + 3 + 67 + 120$ _____

   c $58 - 29$ _____   **d** $125 - 87$ _____

   e 156×50 _____   **f** 49×70 _____

   g $156 \div 5$ _____   **h** $700 \div 25$ _____

2 Working with a friend, make up some similar questions. Then try answering them, one of you using a calculator, the other doing it in their head.

N5 ● DIVISIBILITY RULES

Last digit

Last digit	Number divides exactly by
0, 2, 4, 6, 8	2
0, 5	5
0	10

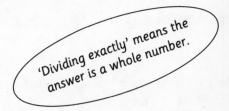
'Dividing exactly' means the answer is a whole number.

Remember that no odd number can be divided exactly by an even number.

Digit sum

• If you add together all the digits of a number, then add together the digits of the answer, and so on, you will end up with a single digit called the **digit sum**.

Example:

$5879 \rightarrow 29$ (from $5+8+7+9$) $\rightarrow 11$ (from $2+9$) $\rightarrow 2$

Digit sum	Number can be divided
3, 6 or 9	3 (and by 6 if the number is even)
9	9

Factors

• A factor divides into another number a whole number of times.

Example:

1, 2, 3, 4, 5, 6, 10, 12, 15, 20, 30 and 60 are factors of 60.

• A **prime number** has exactly two factors, 1 and itself, like 13. A factor which is a prime number is a **prime factor**.

Example:

Write 54 as the product of prime factors.

$54 = 2 \times 27 = 2 \times 3 \times 9 = 2 \times 3 \times 3 \times 3$

or $54 = 2 \times 3^3$

Answer: $54 = 2 \times 3 \times 3 \times 3$ or 2×3^3

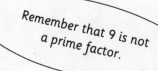
Remember that 9 is not a prime factor.

Multiples

Multiples are produced by multiplying one whole number by another. Some multiples of 7 are 7, 14, 56 and 707.

A **square number** is a **self-multiple**, such as 9 (3 x 3) and 64 (8 x 8).

A

1 Which of 2, 3, 6, 9 and 5 will divide exactly into the following numbers?

   a 468 divides by _____   **b** 855 divides by _____

   c 946 divides by _____   **d** 19 921 362 divides by _____

2 List all the factors of each of these numbers.

   a 30 _____

   b 36 _____

   c 64 _____

   d 192 _____

   e 360 _____

3 Write each of the numbers in question **2** as the product of prime factors.

   a 30 _____

   b 36 _____

   c 64 _____

   d 192 _____

   e 360 _____

N6 ● INVERSE OPERATIONS

Finding the inverse

An inverse operation 'undoes' the effect of an operation.

Examples:

Subtracting 2 is the inverse of adding 2.

Multiplying by 2 is the inverse of dividing by 2.

Finding the square root ($\sqrt{\ }$) is the inverse of squaring.

The square of 7 is 49. The square root of 49 is 7.

Self-inverses

The inverse of some operations is the same operation repeated.

Examples:
Subtracting from
Subtracting 3 from 10 gives 7

Subtracting 7 from 10 gives 3 again.

Dividing into
Dividing 7 into 56 gives 8

Dividing 8 into 56 gives 7 again.

A

1 Write the inverse of these operations.
   a adding 4 _____
   b subtracting 3 _____
   c finding half of _____
   d trebling _____
   e subtracting from 8 _____
   f dividing into 9 _____

2 A number when divided by a half gives 6. What is the number? _____

N7 ● ESTIMATION AND APPROXIMATION

Defining estimation and approximation
- **Estimation** gives a rough idea of size.
- **Approximation** is stating an answer as exactly as required, or as seems sensible.

Examples:

The police might estimate that 10 000 people are watching a football match.

The football club might say the crowd was approximately 12 000, as they knew that 12 345 people had bought tickets.

Estimating answers by approximating
- Round each number in a question so it has only one non-zero digit; then you can work out the answer in your head.

Example:

Estimate the sum, difference, product and quotient of 367 and 2986.

367 is about 400.   2986 is about 3000.

Estimates: sum 3400   difference 2600
                 product 1 200 000   quotient 7 or $\frac{1}{7}$

You must use **approximations** to work out estimations. There is no point in working the answer out exactly, then approximating that!

- Learn sensible sizes for everyday things.
Ask and measure to fill in the answers to these.
Common hourly and weekly wages and annual salaries.
£_____ per hour   £_____ per week   £_____ per year
Height of a door _____ m   a house gutter _____ m
Weight of an adult _____ kg   an egg _____ g
Time to fly to Australia _____ hours
Time to walk a mile _____ minutes
Volume of a bath _____ litres   a medicine spoon _____ ml
Area of a ceiling _____ m^2 a football field _____ m^2

| DO | every time you reach an answer think, 'Is that sensible?' |

If it isn't, try to find your mistake, or at least write a note with a reason why your answer cannot be right.

Rounding
- The last digit in an approximation is increased by 1 if the digit after it is 5, 6, 7, 8 or 9.

Example:

To the nearest ten, 123 is 120, but 126 is 130.

Note: A number rounded to the nearest ten ends with 0.
    A number rounded to the nearest hundred ends with 00.
    A length rounded to the nearest 5 mm must be one of the set:
    {5 mm, 10 mm, 15 mm, 20 mm, 25 mm ...} **or**
    {0.5 cm, 1.0 cm, 1.5 cm, 2.0 cm, 2.5 cm ...}

A

1 I live 180 miles from Heathrow. I have to be there at 1400. I intend to drive and leave my car at the airport. At about what time should I leave home?
I should leave home at _____

2 Abigail decides to save water by having a bath just once a week instead of every day. Estimate how much bath water she will save in a year.
She will save _____

3 Show how you could easily find an approximate answer to each of these.
 a $590 \div 28$ _____
 b $\dfrac{415 \times 296}{78}$ _____
 _____

4 How many 57-seater coaches are needed to transport 1265 rugby fans if each is to have a seat?
_____ coaches are needed.

Decimal place and significant figure approximation
- Numbers correct to *n* **decimal places** are chopped off *n* figures after the decimal point, then rounded.
- Numbers correct to *n* **significant figures** are chopped off *n* figures from the start of the number, or from the first non-zero digit if it starts with zeros, then rounded. The numbers after the *n*th figure but before the decimal point are replaced with zeros.

> Unless told to, do not give measurement answers with more decimal places in your answer than there are in the question.

Examples:

$13.4397 \to 13.4$	to one decimal place
	13.44	to two decimal places
	13.440	to three decimal places
$309.78 \to 309.8$	to four significant figures
	310	to three significant figures
	310	to two significant figures

$0.005699 \to 0.00570$ to three significant figures

> Use FIX n on a calculator to fix the decimal point *n* figures from the end.

> To get 13.440 the 9 has been rounded up to 10, so 0 and carry 1.

> The 0 in 310 (to 2 sf) is to show the empty units column. It is not a significant figure, but cannot be omitted.

DON'T	give answers that are not even near the correct size, e.g. saying 3578 is 36 to two significant figures.
DO	always check your rounded answer IS about the same size as the original one.

Range of error

• When an amount is approximated to a given quantity the **error** is $\pm$ half that quantity.

Example:

15.5 cm is correct to the nearest 5 mm.

The largest it can be is $15.5\,\text{cm} + 2.5\,\text{mm} = 15.75\,\text{cm}$

The smallest it can be is $15.5\,\text{cm} - 2.5\,\text{mm} = 15.25\,\text{cm}$

B

1 If your calculator has a decimal places key (usually marked FIX or F) set it to three decimal places and investigate how it deals with numbers.

2 Giving your answer to three significant figures, use a calculator to evaluate these.
   a $1000 \div 7$ _____
   b $\sqrt{2}$ _____
   c π _____
   d 4756×909 _____
   e $14 \div 976$ _____

3 Geraldine weighs 69 kg to the nearest $\frac{1}{4}$ kg. What is the largest and the smallest weight she could be?
   Largest _____ Smallest _____

4 A component has to have a diameter of 97.5 mm with a tolerance of ± 0.1 mm.
   a What is the range of error? _____
   b The measuring instrument reads to the nearest 0.1 mm. At what measurements should components start to be rejected? _____

N8 ● PROBLEMS USING THE FOUR RULES AND A CALCULATOR

Steps to solving problems
- Think carefully about which of the four rules you should use.
- Check that your answer seems sensible. You would not pay £1200 to fill a car fuel tank, or £1500 for a household gas bill!
- Use your calculator efficiently, e.g. use memory and brackets instead of writing down intermediate steps.
- Learn to interpret calculator rounding errors.

Example:
Juliette drives 360 miles, averaging 7 miles per litre. How much will the petrol for the journey cost her at 53p per litre?

Juliette will need about $360 \div 7$ litres.

This will cost her $360 \div 7 \times 53$ pence.

| 3 | 6 | 0 | ÷ | 7 | × | 5 | 3 | = |

Answer: Juliette's petrol will cost about £27.26.

This gives a display of 2725.7143, but do not write this as the answer.

---

1 Karen has three times as many cats as Liam, who has two fewer than Sean.
   a Why can't you tell who has the most cats?

   _____

   _____

   b Karen has six cats. How many does Sean have? _____ cats

2 John is paid 30p per mile travelling expenses. He travels 11 900 miles one year, averaging 7 miles per litre.
   a How much should he be paid? £_____
   b The petrol costs 51.5p per litre. What is his petrol bill for the year? £_____

3 Rose has to cut nine window bars, each of length 825 mm. How many four-metre lengths of steel should she buy?

   _____ lengths

   1 metre (m) = 1000 millimetres (mm)

4 Taking 11 gallons to be 50 litres, how many five-litre cans can be filled from one 100-gallon tank?

   _____ cans

N9 ● NEGATIVE NUMBERS

Using a calculator for directed numbers
• To enter a **negative** number use the $\boxed{+/-}$ key. At the time of writing, most calculators require the number to be showing in the window **before** you press the $\boxed{+/-}$ key.

A directed number may be positive or negative.

The $\boxed{-}$ key is an operator key which is used to take away. Do not use it to enter a minus sign.

Ordering negative numbers
• **Negative** numbers are below zero (to the left of zero on a number line). A negative number is taken as less than another if it is further from zero. Strictly, the smallest possible value of anything is zero, and -3 and $+3$ are the same size but in opposite directions.

Example:
These numbers are in decreasing order of size.

| 2.4 | 2.35 | 0 | -0.5 | -0.6 | -0.75 | -1 | -2.3 |

DON'T think that -0.6 is 'bigger' than -0.5.

DO remember the number line, where -0.6 is further from zero than -0.5 is.

Addition and subtraction
• Think of movement along the number line.
• To take away a negative number you add its positive equivalent, that is $--$ changes to $+$.

Example:
Find $-4+ -5$.

This means 'start at -4 and go down another 5'.

Answer: $-4+ -5 = -9$

Example:
Find $-4- -5$.

$- -5$ becomes $+5$.

$-4+5$ means 'start at -4 and go up 5'.

Answer: $-4- -5 = +1$ or just 1

Multiplication and division
• Multiplying and dividing any number by a negative number changes its sign.
So   'plus' multiplied or divided by 'minus' is 'minus'
and   'minus' multiplied or divided by 'minus' is 'plus'.

Examples:
$7 \times -8 = -56$

$-7 \times -7 = +49$ or just 49

Substitution into formulae

Example:
When $b = -1$ and $c = -2$

$$4 - b = 4 - -1 = 4 + 1 = 5$$

$$bc = -1 \times -2 = 2$$

$$\frac{6}{1 - 2bc} = \frac{6}{1 - (2 \times -1 \times -2)} = \frac{6}{1 - 4} = \frac{6}{-3} = -2$$

> To work out $2 \times -1 \times -2$:
> 2 times -1 is -2,
> then -2 times -2 is 4,
> 'minus' times 'minus' is 'plus'.

DON'T	think that $-a - a = +2a$
DO	remember to think of moving along a number line.

DON'T	learn 'two minuses make a plus', because rules that are not always true are dangerous.
DO	learn: 'Minus minus makes plus,' and: 'Minus times minus makes plus.'

> If you have already learnt 'two minuses make a plus', forget it!

DON'T	say $1^2 = 2$, especially when substituting, e.g. 'If $a = 1$ then $a^2 = 2$'. (It should be 1 of course.)
DO	remember '1 times 1 is 1, times 1 is 1, times 1 is 1, times 1 is . . .!!'

A

1 Arrange these numbers in order of size, from smallest to greatest.

$$0.1 \qquad -0.5 \qquad -0.56 \qquad -0.4 \qquad -1 \qquad -0.08 \qquad -0.101$$

> Here, smaller means further down the number line.

2 Given that $a = -3$ and $c = -1$, evaluate each expression.

a $a + c$ _____ **b** $a - c$ _____

c $c - a$ _____ **d** $3 + c$ _____

e $ac \ (a \times c)$ _____ **f** ca _____

g $a \div c$ _____ **h** c^2 _____

i $6 \div a$ _____ **j** $6 \div ac$ _____

> To evaluate is to work out the value of.

N10 ● COMMON FRACTIONS

Kinds of fraction

- $\frac{3}{4}$ and $\frac{6}{7}$ are examples of **common fractions**.
- The number at the bottom (called the **denominator**) tells you how many equal pieces the whole is divided into.
- The number at the top (called the **numerator**) tells you how many of the pieces are involved.
  So $\frac{6}{7}$ means you have six of the seven pieces the whole is cut into.
- A **mixed number** involves both a whole number and a common fraction, like $5\frac{1}{4}$. Mixed numbers can be changed into **top-heavy fractions.**

> Common fractions are also called **vulgar fractions**.

Example:

$6\frac{3}{4} = \frac{27}{4}$

6 is 6×4 quarters = 24 quarters plus the 3 quarters gives 27 quarters.

> The correct name for a top-heavy fraction is **improper**.

- **Equivalent fractions** are of equal value. They can be made by multiplying (or dividing) both the top and bottom numbers by the same factor.

Examples:

$\frac{2}{5}$ is equivalent to $\frac{22}{55}$ (multiplying both 2 and 5 by 11).

$\frac{6}{8}$ is equivalent to $\frac{3}{4}$ (dividing both 6 and 8 by 2).

> Equivalent fractions are also known as **like fractions**.

Finding a fraction of a quantity

Example:
Find $\frac{5}{8}$ of £24.

We first find $\frac{1}{8}$ of £24 by dividing it by 8, giving £3.

Now we take 5 of these parts, giving £15.

Answer: $\frac{5}{8}$ of £24 = £15

Example:
Multiply 30 by $3\frac{2}{5}$.

Multiply 30 by 3, giving 90.

Multiply 30 by $\frac{2}{5}$ by dividing by 5, then multiplying by 2, giving $6 \times 2 = 12$.

Altogether, $90 + 12 = 102$.

Answer: $30 \times 3\frac{2}{5} = 102$

Fractional changes

Example:
The price of a ruler goes up by a quarter. At first it cost 16 pence. What does it cost now?

$\frac{1}{4}$ of 16 pence = 4 pence.

The price is now 16 pence + 4 pence = 20 pence.

Answer: It now costs 20 pence.

A

1 George has covered $\frac{4}{9}$ of his planned journey. What fraction has he still to go?

_____

2 Simplify the fraction $\frac{36}{135}$.

_____

3 Complete these equivalent fractions.

a $\dfrac{5}{6} = \dfrac{15}{}$ **b** $\dfrac{2}{5} = \dfrac{}{35}$ **c** $6\frac{3}{4} = \dfrac{}{4}$

4 In question **1** George's planned journey was 648 km. How many kilometres has he covered?

_____ km

5 This table shows the proportion of the Council Tax to be paid in each of the bands A to H.
Work out how much will be paid in each band when the Council Tax is £450. Write the answers below.

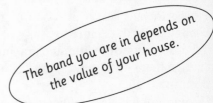
The band you are in depends on the value of your house.

Band	A	B	C	D	E	F	G	H
Pay	$\frac{2}{3}$	$\frac{7}{9}$	$\frac{8}{9}$	1	$1\frac{2}{9}$	$1\frac{4}{9}$	$1\frac{2}{3}$	2
Amount (£)								

A single occupant would pay less than these amounts.

Conversion between decimal and common fractions

- To change a common fraction to a **decimal fraction**, divide the top number by the bottom.

Example:
$\frac{3}{8} \rightarrow 3 \div 8 = 0.375$

- To change a decimal fraction to a common fraction, write a 1 under the decimal point and a zero under each decimal place, then cancel to make it as simple as possible.

Example:
$0.015 \rightarrow \dfrac{15}{1000} = \dfrac{3}{200}$

The 5 of 0.015 is in the thousandths column.

Recurring decimals

Many fractions do not work out to exact or **terminating** decimals. Instead the figures keep on repeating or **recurring**.

For example, $\frac{1}{7}$ is $0.142\,857\,142\,857\,142\,857\ldots$

We write this as $0.\dot{1}42\,85\dot{7}$.

- Change a recurring decimal to a common fraction by writing the recurring part over as many 9s as there are figures in the recurring part.

Example:

$0.\dot{1}\dot{6} = \dfrac{16}{99}$

Ordering fractions

- Unless the answer is very obvious, the easiest way to order fractions is to change them to decimals.
  To order fractions without changing them to decimals you have to change them until they all have either the same top number or the same bottom number.
- Here is a quick way to find which is the bigger of two fractions, for example $\frac{7}{9}$ and $\frac{18}{23}$.

$$7 \times 23 = 161 \qquad\qquad 9 \times 18 = 162$$

$$\frac{7}{9} \diagdown\!\!\!\diagup \frac{18}{23}$$

162 is bigger than 161 so $\dfrac{18}{23}$ is bigger than $\dfrac{7}{9}$.

B

1 Write each of these as a decimal fraction.

  a $\frac{3}{5}$ _____   **b** $\frac{4}{100}$ _____

  c $\frac{7}{9}$ _____   **d** $\frac{3}{11}$ _____

2 Write each of these as a common fraction as simply as possible.

  a 0.07 _____   **b** 0.15 _____

  c 0.003 _____   **d** 0.016 _____

3 What common fraction is each of these?

  a 0.3 _____   **b** $0.\dot{3}$ _____

  c $0.\dot{1}$ _____   **d** $0.\dot{3}\dot{5}$ _____

  e $0.\dot{1}3\dot{2}$ _____

4 Place these in order of size, smallest first.

  a $\frac{3}{8}$ $\frac{3}{20}$ $\frac{3}{10}$ $\frac{3}{7}$ _____

  b $\frac{5}{8}$ $\frac{4}{11}$ $\frac{1}{2}$ $\frac{99}{100}$ _____

N11 ● CALCULATING WITH FRACTIONS

Fraction calculators

- You need to be able to add or subtract and multiply or divide fractions. The National Curriculum allows you to use a fractional calculator to do this. However, you will need to know the written methods to do higher algebra.

Multiplying fractions

- Multiply the top numbers together; multiply the bottom numbers together.

Example:

$$\frac{4}{9} \times \frac{7}{11} = \frac{28}{99}$$

- Sometimes the numbers can be made simpler by **cancelling**, which is dividing one of the top numbers and one of the bottom numbers by the same number.

Example:

$$\overset{4}{\underset{9}{\cancel{\frac{16}{27}}}} \times \overset{\overset{1}{\cancel{3}}}{\underset{\underset{1}{\cancel{4}}}{\cancel{\frac{36}{48}}}} = \frac{4}{9}$$

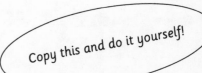

Copy this and do it yourself!

- When multiplying mixed numbers, first change them into top-heavy fractions (see Section N10).

Dividing fractions

- First change any mixed numbers to top-heavy fractions. Then change the sign to 'multiply' and invert the second fraction. Invert here means turn upside-down.

Example:

$$\frac{5}{16} \div 7\tfrac{1}{2} \rightarrow \frac{5}{16} \div \frac{15}{2} \rightarrow \underset{8}{\cancel{\frac{5}{16}}}^{1} \times \underset{3}{\cancel{\frac{2}{15}}}^{1} = \frac{1}{24}$$

Adding fractions

- Both fractions must have the same bottom number before you can add them. This bottom number must be a multiple of both the original bottom numbers. Try to choose the smallest multiple possible.

Examples:

$$\frac{3}{4} + \frac{5}{8} \rightarrow \frac{6}{8} + \frac{5}{8} = \frac{11}{8} = 1\tfrac{3}{8}$$

$$\frac{7}{9} + \frac{1}{6} \rightarrow \frac{14}{18} + \frac{3}{18} = \frac{17}{18}$$

- When mixed numbers have to be added, add the whole numbers first, then add the fractions.

Subtracting fractions

- This is done in the same way as addition. A difficulty can arise when mixed numbers are involved.

Example:

$8\frac{1}{4} - 5\frac{3}{7}$

The whole numbers give $8 - 5 = 3$.

The fractions give $\dfrac{1}{4} - \dfrac{3}{7} \rightarrow \dfrac{7}{28} - \dfrac{12}{28}$.

The problem is that 7 is smaller than 12.

However you should know that $7 - 12 = -5$.

So the answer is $3 - \dfrac{5}{28} = 2\frac{23}{28}$.

Answer: $8\frac{1}{4} - 5\frac{3}{7} = 2\frac{23}{28}$

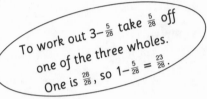

To work out $3 - \frac{5}{28}$ take $\frac{5}{28}$ off one of the three wholes. One is $\frac{28}{28}$, so $1 - \frac{5}{28} = \frac{23}{28}$.

A

1 When $a = \frac{4}{5}$, $b = 3\frac{2}{3}$ and $c = 2\frac{5}{6}$ find the value of each of these.

a $a \times b$

b $b \times c$

c $c \div a$

d $b \div c$

e $a + b$

f $b + c$

g $c - a$

h $b - c$

N12 ● PERCENTAGES

Defining a percentage

- 15% of something means $\frac{15}{100}$ of it, or 0.15 of it.

  8% of something means $\frac{8}{100}$ of it, or 0.08 of it.

Percentages of quantities

Example:

Find 8% of £25.

8% is 0.08, so work out 0.08×25 to give £2.

Answer: 8% of £25 = £2.

Fraction to percentage

- To express a fraction as a percentage find what fraction of 100 it is.

Example:

To find $\frac{3}{4}$ as a percentage work out $\frac{3}{4} \times 100$.

| 3 | $\div$ | 4 | $\times$ | 1 | 0 | 0 | $=$ |

- To express one quantity as a percentage of another quantity, write the first over the second to form a fraction, then convert the fraction to a percentage.

Example:

A price is decreased from £450 to £400. What is the percentage reduction?

The original £450 is reduced by £50.

So the reduction is $\frac{50}{450} \times 100\% = 11.1\%$.

Answer: The percentage reduction is 11.1%.

- **Learn:** **Change per cent** is change over original, multiplied by 100.
- **Learn:** **Percentage error** is error over true value, multiplied by 100.

To change by a given percentage

- To **increase** by $r\%$, multiply by $\dfrac{100+r}{100}$.

- To **decrease** by $r\%$, multiply by $\dfrac{100-r}{100}$.

Examples:

To increase by $7\frac{1}{2}\%$ multiply by 1.075.

To decrease by $8\frac{1}{4}\%$ multiply by 0.9175.

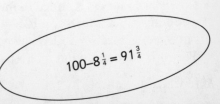

$$100 - 8\tfrac{1}{4} = 91\tfrac{3}{4}$$

A

1 Express each of these as a decimal fraction.
   a 48% _____   b 7% _____
   c 12¼% _____   d 6¾% _____

2 Find 46% of 230 metres.

_____ m

3 Jenny is 7. Her dad is 35. Express Jenny's age as a percentage of her dad's.

_____ %

4 Hi Lo buys a game for £15 and sells it for £9. Express the loss as a percentage of
   the cost price.

_____ %

5 Francis cuts his weight from 93 kg to 85 kg. By what percentage has he reduced
   his weight?

_____ %

6 A grant of £125m is cut by 5½%. What is the new grant?

£_____

7 Increase £925 000 by 12%.

£_____

8 Henry estimated that he had enough petrol to drive the 85 miles home, but ran
   out 5 miles from his house. What percentage error did he make?

_____ %

Interest

- Interest is paid when money, called the **principal**, is lent or borrowed. The
  interest on £250 at 5% per year would be £250 × 0.05 = £12.50 per year.
  The **amount** (principal plus interest) is £262.50.
- **Compound interest** is added to the amount. **Simple interest** is not.
  The compound interest on £250 at 5% p.a. would be £12.50 the first year,
  but 5% of £262.50 = £13.12 the next year.
  To work out compound interest

  repeatedly multiply by $1 + \dfrac{r}{100}$ where $r\%$ is the **rate of interest**.

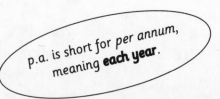

p.a. is short for *per annum*, meaning **each year**.

Example:
Find the compound interest on £100 at 7.5% p.a. over five years.

$1 + \frac{7.5}{100} = 1.075$

The final amount will be

£100 × 1.075 × 1.075 × 1.075 × 1.075 × 1.075
= £143.56

Answer: The compound interest is £43.56.

Use the constant multiplier on your calculator.

B

1 Find the compound interest on:

a £200 at 8% for ten years   £_____

b £1000 at 4½% for six years.   £_____

N13 ● RATIOS AND SCALES

Simplifying ratios

- A **ratio** shows the connection between two quantities.
- A ratio can be written using a colon (:), but only if both amounts are in the same units.
- Ratios can be simplified, like fractions, by dividing both numbers by the same factor.

Example:

The Earth's atmosphere is about 78% nitrogen and 21% oxygen by volume.

The ratio of nitrogen to oxygen is 78:21.

Dividing 78 and 21 by 3, this simplifies to 26:7.

The other 1% is mainly argon, with about 0.04% carbon dioxide.

Unitary ratios

- Ratios are easier to understand and use if they are given as $1:n$ or $n:1$, for example a ratio of 3 to 1.

Example:

Change 8:25 into **a** $1:n$ form and **b** $n:1$ form.

a To change the 8 to 1, divide both numbers by 8, giving 1:3.125.

b To change the 25 to 1, divide both numbers by 25, giving 0.32:1.

Dividing in a ratio

Example:

Divide 100 kg in the ratio 7:3.

$7 + 3$ makes 10 parts. $100 \text{ kg} \div 10 = 10 \text{ kg}$.

$7 \times 10 \text{ kg} = 70 \text{ kg}$ and $3 \times 10 \text{ kg} = 30 \text{ kg}$.

Answer: 70 kg and 30 kg

*The correct name for dividing in a ratio is **proportional division**.*

Given one part of a ratio, to find the other

- Multiply the given amount by a fraction made up from the ratio. Decide which way up to write the fraction by thinking whether the answer amount will be bigger or smaller than the given amount.

Example:

A jam is made with fruit to sugar in the ratio 4:3 by weight. How much sugar is needed for 6 kg of fruit?

The 4 parts of fruit is 6 kg.

The 3 parts of sugar is $6 \text{ kg} \times \frac{3}{4} = 4\frac{1}{2} \text{ kg}$.

Increasing and decreasing in a ratio

- To change in the ratio $a:b$ multiply by $\dfrac{a}{b}$.

Example:
A photograph measuring 6 inches by $4\frac{1}{2}$ inches is enlarged in the ratio $7:5$.

The $4\frac{1}{2}$-inch length becomes $\dfrac{7}{5} \times \dfrac{9}{2} = 6.3$ inches.

DON'T mix up the method to share out in a ratio with the method to change in a ratio.
DO only add the ratio figures to give the total number of parts when sharing out an amount.

Map scales and the representative fraction

If a map has a **scale** '1 cm represents 1 km', then 1 cm represents
$1000\,\text{m} = 100\,000\,\text{cm}$. The **representative fraction** is $\frac{1}{100\,000}$ or $1:100\,000$.

A

1 A ring is to contain a mixture of gold and silver in the ratio 5:11. How much silver should be added to 25 grams of gold?

_____ g

2 At a party there are 98 boys and girls in the ratio 3:4. How many boys are there at the party?

_____ boys

3 A map has a scale of 1 cm representing 25 km. What is the representative fraction?

_____

4 A company issues new shares at the rate of five new shares at 95p each for every eight already held.
   a How many shares will be offered to Bea who already has 1500?

_____

   b Bea buys all the shares she is offered. What is the ratio of her new holding to her old holding?

_____

N14 ● USING A CALCULATOR

Other notes will be found on pages 18, 33, 72 and 81.

Memory

- **Store memory** loses the previous stored number when you use it. It may be marked $\boxed{\text{Min}}$, $\boxed{\text{STO}}$, $\boxed{\text{x} \rightarrow \text{M}}$, etc.
- **Accumulating memory** adds the display to the previously stored amount. It may be marked $\boxed{\text{SUM}}$, $\boxed{\text{ACC}}$, $\boxed{\text{M+}}$, etc.
- If your calculator has only one memory you *must* cancel it before starting to accumulate.

> **DON'T** use the accumulating memory to store if you have a store memory.
>
> **DO** check the accumulating memory is empty (no M showing in the window) before you start.

Constant function $\boxed{\text{k}}$

This repeats an operation on the displayed number when $\boxed{=}$ is pressed. Some calculators always have the constant function active. Some switch it on when you press the function key twice. Some use a $\boxed{\text{k}}$ key.

A key marked $\boxed{\text{EXC}}$ or $\boxed{\text{x}<-->\text{M}}$ lets you exchange the memory and the display.

Experiment with *your* calculator!

Brackets/BODMAS

- BODMAS is the rule followed by scientific calculators. It stands for 'Brackets first, then do the Dividing and Multiplying, then Addition and Subtraction.'

  So a scientific calculator will work out $2 + 2 \times 2$ as 6, not 8.
- Your calculator can easily mistake what you really want it to do, especially when fractions are involved. This is where using the memory or brackets is necessary.

BODMAS is sometimes called **algebraic logic**.

Practise using calculator methods where no answers are written until the end.

Example:

$\dfrac{5+7}{3 \times 2}$ is $12 \div 6$, so the answer is 2.

If you key in $\boxed{5}$ $\boxed{+}$ $\boxed{7}$ $\boxed{\div}$ $\boxed{3}$ $\boxed{\times}$ $\boxed{2}$ $\boxed{=}$

the calculator will work out $5 + (\frac{7}{3} \times 2)$ and give the answer as 9.6.

Correct method using brackets:

$\boxed{(}$ $\boxed{5}$ $\boxed{+}$ $\boxed{7}$ $\boxed{)}$ $\boxed{\div}$ $\boxed{(}$ $\boxed{3}$ $\boxed{\times}$ $\boxed{2}$ $\boxed{)}$ $\boxed{=}$

Correct method using memory:

$\boxed{3}$ $\boxed{\times}$ $\boxed{2}$ $\boxed{=}$ $\boxed{\text{STO}}$ $\boxed{5}$ $\boxed{+}$ $\boxed{7}$ $\boxed{=}$ $\boxed{\div}$ $\boxed{\text{MR}}$ $\boxed{=}$

Bracket method
You could press $\boxed{=}$ at the end of the top line instead of putting it in brackets, though this could cause a wrong answer if the fraction is part of another complex expression.

Memory method
Note that you work out the bottom of the fraction first.

A

1 Use $\boxed{\text{M}+}$ to find $6+3+5+6+5+8+9+4+7$. _____

2 Use a calculator to divide £307.20 equally among 16 people.   £_____

3 VAT at 17.5% has to be added to lots of prices. Using the constant multiplier ($\times 1.175$) add the VAT to the following.

a £35 _____   **b** £12.40 _____

c £230 _____   **d** £68.75 _____

e £82.45 _____   **f** £930 _____

4 List the key presses you would need to calculate $\dfrac{6.7 \div 7}{4.5 \times 4.9}$ using the bracket keys.

5 Repeat question **4** but use the memory instead of brackets.

Trial and improvement

You can use a calculator to help you home in on a correct answer to a complex expression.

Example:

Cora does not know she could use the $\boxed{x^{1/y}}$ key to find $\sqrt[3]{10}$. Instead she estimates the answer to be 2, then works as follows.

$2 \times 2 \times 2 = 8$	too small
$2.5 \times 2.5 \times 2.5 = 15.625$	too big
$2.3 \times 2.3 \times 2.3 = 12.167$	too big
$2.2 \times 2.2 \times 2.2 = 10.648$	too big
$2.15 \times 2.15 \times 2.15 = 9.938375$	too small
$2.17 \times 2.17 \times 2.17 = 10.218313$	too big

She uses the constant multiplier function to save time, and the memory to store each try.

she continues until the answer is as near as she wants.

> **DON'T** give your last display as the question answer, e.g. writing 10.22 as the answer to the above example, instead of 2.17.

Powers and roots

- Powers (such as 5^5 meaning $5 \times 5 \times 5 \times 5 \times 5$) can be worked out using the constant function.
- There is always a square root key $\boxed{\sqrt{}}$ and often a cube root key $\boxed{\sqrt[3]{}}$.
- Powers may also be worked out using the y^x key (labelled x^y on Casio calculators).

The cube root of 8 is 2, because $2 \times 2 \times 2 = 8$.

Example:

5^6 or $5 \times 5 \times 5 \times 5 \times 5 \times 5$ can be found by:

$\boxed{5}$ $\boxed{y^x}$ $\boxed{6}$ $\boxed{=}$

- Roots may be written using a **reciprocal index notation**.
  So $\sqrt{4}$ is written $4^{1/2}$ and $6^{1/4}$ is the fourth root of 6.
  The root key may be labelled $\boxed{y^{1/x}}$ ($\boxed{x^{1/y}}$ on Casio!) or $\boxed{\sqrt[x]{y}}$.
  It is often a $\boxed{\text{SHIFT}}$, $\boxed{\text{2nd F}}$ or $\boxed{\text{INV}}$ above the power key.

Example:

$6^{1/4}$ (the fourth root of 6) can be found by:

$\boxed{6}$ $\boxed{y^{1/x}}$ $\boxed{4}$ $\boxed{=}$

Many roots do not have exact values.

B

1 John is finding $\sqrt[4]{20}$ using trial and improvement. He can see it is between 2 and 3, because $2^4 = 16$ and $3^4 = 81$. Continue John's method to find $\sqrt[4]{20}$ correct to three decimal places.

$$\sqrt[4]{20} = \underline{\hspace{3cm}}$$

2 Use the power and root keys to find these, correct to four significant figures.

  a 1.6^8 _____

  b $\sqrt[5]{0.25}$ _____

3 Use the fewest key presses possible to work this out.

$$\frac{0.605 \div 15^4}{(5 \div 7) - 0.5}$$

Number of presses _____

N15 ● STANDARD FORM/SCIENTIFIC NOTATION

Writing numbers in standard form

3.06×10^4 is a number in standard form or scientific notation.

The standard form is $\qquad a \times 10^n$

where a is a number from 1 to 9.9.

The value of n tells you how many columns to move the figures to write a in normal notation. Make a bigger if n is positive, make a smaller if n is negative.

So $\quad 3.06 \times 10^4$ is 30 600

and $\quad 3.06 \times 10^{-4}$ is 0.000306.

Scientific notation is sometimes written SCI.

Using a calculator

Scientific calculators display answers in scientific notation when they are too big or too small to be shown in normal notation. Try
1 000 000 000 × 1 000 000 000.

Use the $\boxed{\text{EXP}}$ or $\boxed{\text{EE}}$ key to enter a number in scientific notation.

A calculator displays 3.06×10^4 as 3.06   04.

Note that you do not key in the multiplication sign or the 10.

> **DON'T** write the calculator display 3.06   04 like that on paper.
> **DO** write standard form as $a \times 10^n$, i.e. 3.06×10^4.

You can usually change the mode of the calculator so that all numbers are displayed in scientific notation (mode SCI). Some switch into this mode automatically once you type in one number in scientific notation.
Use mode Normal to return to normal notation (assuming the answer is not too big to be displayed this way).

A

1 Write these populations (1993 figures) in standard form correct to three significant figures.

New York   7 322 564 _____   London   6 678 699 _____

India   843 930 861 _____   Monaco   24 687 _____

2 Write these sizes in standard form.
   Thickness of £10 note   0.05 mm _____
   Thickness of human hair   between 0.03 and 0.075 mm _____
   Diameter of red blood cell   0.007 mm _____

3 $h = 3.56 \times 10^3$ $k = 2.04 \times 10^{-2}$ $m = 8.9 \times 10^5$ $t = 5.79 \times 10^{-1}$

   Find the values of these in standard form correct to 2 decimal places.
   a $h \times k$ _____   **b** $(h+k) \div (m-t)$ _____

   c t^2 _____   **d** $2m - (t-k)$ _____

4 It has been said that the whole population of the world, estimated to be 5 292 000 000 in 1993, could stand on the Isle of Wight, area 381 km². Is it true?

N16 ● GRAPHS OF REAL-LIFE SITUATIONS

Graphing real-life situations

The following figures illustrate some examples.

Figures N16:1 and N16:2 are travel graphs. Figure N16:1 shows distance travelled, time taken and speed. The sloping straight line shows that after five minutes the speed was about 1 km/min, or 60 km/h, travelling back towards the start. Figure N16:2 is a speed-time graph. The slope of the line represents acceleration and deceleration.

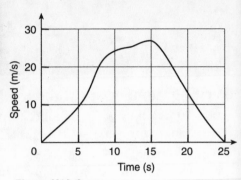

Figure N16:2

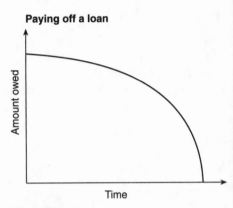

Figure N16:3

Figure N16:1

The graphs in Figures N16:3 and N16:4 illustrate growth and decay, that is, how the quantity increases and/or decreases as time passes.
Now work out what Figures N16:5 and N16:6 show!

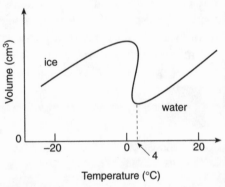

Figure N16:4

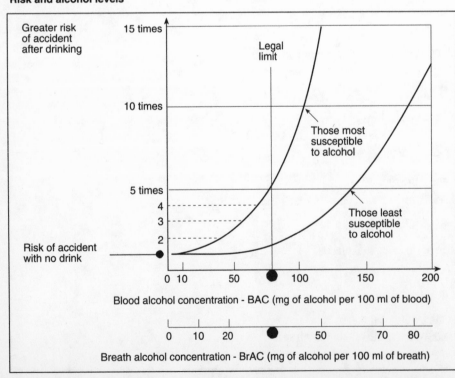

Figure N16:5

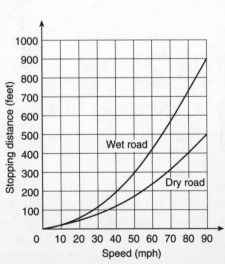

Figure N16:6

A

1 Figure N16:7 shows four flasks which are to be filled with water running in at a constant rate.

Figure N16:7

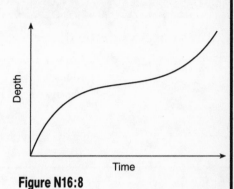

Figure N16:8

a Figure N16:8 belongs to one of the flasks. Which one? _____
b Draw similar graphs for each of the other flasks.
c Draw graphs to show how the diameters of the water surfaces change with time.

2 Figure N16:9 shows a fairground ride.

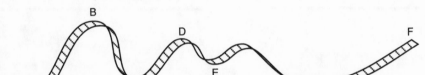

Figure N16:9

Figure N16:10 represents part of the ride between two of the marked letters.
a Which part does it show? _____
b Draw a graph for the whole ride.

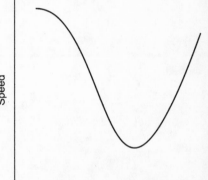

Figure N16:10

3 Using axes, time from 1200 to 1400, distance 0 to 30 miles from the start, draw a travel graph to show a journey starting at 1200, averaging 30 mph for one hour, followed by a rest of half an hour, then returning to the start at an average speed of 60 mph.

4 In Figure N16:11 Toby and Ella travel on the same route. Describe their journeys, including where they pass each other. _____
_____
_____

5 The graph in Figure N16:12 appeared in a newspaper. Comment on it. _____

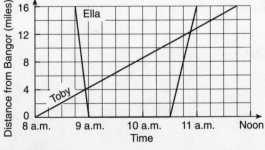

Figure N16:11

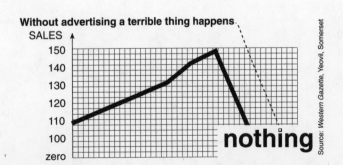

Figure N16:12

A1 ● USING ALGEBRAIC NOTATION

Expressing symbolically

Algebraic shorthand: bc means $b \times c$

b^2 means $b \times b$

c^4 means $c \times c \times c \times c$.

$\dfrac{d}{e}$ means d divided by e.

Notation is the system of symbols used in writing algebraic expressions.

c^4 is also called 'c raised to the power 4'.

DON'T read $2b^2$ as $2b \times 2b$.

DO remember the INDEX (raised figure) only applies to the letter by which it is written. $2b^2$ is $2 \times b^2$ or $2 \times b \times b$

A

1 Let $a = 3$, $b = 5$, $c = 1$, $d = -1$ and $e = -2$.

State the value of each of these.

a ab _____

b c^2 _____

c d^2 _____

d $2ab$ _____

e $2a^2$ _____

f $2b^2$ _____

g $a-e$ _____

h $2c^2-3d^2$ _____

i $\dfrac{2a-3e}{4d}$ _____

j $\dfrac{4b^2}{de}$ _____

Formulae expressed in words

*A **formula** is a recipe to make something.*

Example:

The tariff for a taxi is a fixed charge of 50p per person, plus 25p per minute.

Two passengers make a ten-minute journey. What is the fare?

Answer: $(2 \times 50p) + (10 \times 25p) = £3.50$

Example:

A camel is bought for a third of the original asking price, plus the purchase of the saddle for 150 shekels. The buyer hands over 2000 shekels. What was the original price of the camel?

Answer: The camel was bought for $2000 - 150 = 1850$ shekels.

Its original price was $3 \times 1850 = 5550$ shekels.

B

1 Jody's Babysitters charge a flat rate of £3 per child, then £2 per hour or part-hour up to 10 p.m. and 50p for each ten minutes, or part ten-minutes, after 10 p.m. What would be the charge for a babysitter for two children from 7.30 p.m. until midnight?

£_____

2 The gravitational pull, in newtons, between two objects is found by multiplying together their masses (in tonnes), then multiplying by 67 and dividing by the square of the distance between them (in metres). What is the gravitational pull between two asteroids of mass 5000 and 25 000 tonnes when they are 100 km (100 000 m) apart?

_____ N

Formulae expressed in symbols

Example:
Climate temperatures are usually measured in degrees Fahrenheit (°F) or degrees Celsius (°C).

The formula to convert °C to °F is

$$F = \frac{9C}{5} + 32.$$

C

1 Use the above formula to convert these temperatures to °F.
  a 30°C _____°F
  b −40°C _____°F

2 The solutions of the equation $ax^2 + bx + c = 0$ are given by these formulae.

$$x = \frac{-b + \sqrt{(b^2 - 4ac)}}{2a} \quad \text{and} \quad x = \frac{-b - \sqrt{(b^2 - 4ac)}}{2a}$$

For the equation $2x^2 + 9x + 4 = 0$, $a = 2$, $b = 9$ and $c = 4$.

Find:
  a b^2 _____   **b** $4ac$ _____
  c $b^2 - 4ac$ _____   **d** $\sqrt{(b^2 - 4ac)}$ _____
  e the two possible values for x.

_____ and _____

3 Find the solutions of the equation $x^2 + 2x - 3 = 0$.

_____ and _____

A2 ● MANIPULATING ALGEBRAIC EXPRESSIONS

Collecting terms

Like terms contain the same letters, and the same powers of those letters, for example $3h$ and $5h$, $4a^2$ and a^2, $6a^3b$ and $7a^3b$. Like terms may be added and subtracted. Unlike terms cannot, so be careful!

Examples:

$2 - 2a + 3a = 2 + a$

$2 + a$ cannot be simplified.

$3a^2 - 6 + a^2 = 4a^2 - 6$

DON'T   give the answer to $4 - 4a + 3a$ as $4 - 7a$.

DO   give the answer to $4 - 4a + 3a$ as $4 - a$.

$-2a + 3a$ is not $-5a$

Simplified means written in a shorter form.

The minus sign in $3a^2 - 6 + a^2$ belongs to the 6, so it is **not** $3a^2 - a^2 = 2a^2$

Multiplying terms

- When multiplying terms with the same letter, the rule is to **add the indices**.

   $a^2 \times a^3$ means $(a \times a) \times (a \times a \times a)$ which is a^5.

   The rule can be written as

$$a^m \times a^n = a^{m+n}$$

   So $a^2 \times a^3 = a^{2+3} = a^5$.

Examples:

$4a^2b^3c \times 4ab^3cd = 16a^3b^6c^2d$

$\qquad 3a^2h \times 4n = 12a^2hn$

$\qquad 2c^3 \times ac^5 = 2ac^8$

Take one thing at a time in your head, 4×4, then $a^2 \times a$, and so on.

Dividing terms

- Division in algebra is usually written as a fraction.
- If possible the fraction is then simplified by **cancelling**.

Example:

$$6a^2b \div 8d = \frac{6a^2b}{8d} \xrightarrow{\div 2}[\div 2]{} = \frac{3a^2b}{4d}$$

Cancelling is dividing both top and bottom of a fraction by the same number.

- Letter terms can be simplified by subtracting their indices.

$$\frac{a^5}{a^3} = \frac{a \times a \times a \times a \times a}{a \times a \times a} = \frac{\cancel{a} \times \cancel{a} \times \cancel{a} \times a \times a}{\cancel{a} \times \cancel{a} \times \cancel{a}} = a^2$$

   or $a^5 \div a^3 = a^{5-3} = a^2$.

   The rule can be written as

$$a^m \div a^n = a^{m-n}$$

A

1 Simplify these.

a $5a - 3a - 4 + 9$

b $4 - 2a + a$

c $6 + 8 - 8a + 8a$

d $e - 2e - 5 + 6$

e $3er - 5e + 2 + 5er - 2e - e$

f $3a^2g - 3a^2g + ag$

2 Simplify these.

a $4af \times a$

b $3gh \times 4g^2$

c $2a^2c \times 3a^3cd$

d $5 \times 4e^4fg \times 2f$

3 Simplify these.

a $6d \div 3d$

b $\dfrac{4a^2}{2a}$

c $\dfrac{6a^5b}{2a^3}$

d $\dfrac{12x^3y^2z}{24x^3y^3z^2}$

Removing brackets

- A term written in front of a bracket multiplies every term inside the bracket.

Removing brackets is also called **expanding**.

Example:
$$h(2h + 3ah^2) = 2h^2 + 3ah^3$$

DON'T add before you have done any multiplication.

Example:
$$6 + 2(a - 1) = 6 + 2a - 2 = 4 + 2a$$

not $8(a - 1) = 8a - 1$!

- When there are two pairs of brackets, each term in the first multiplies each term in the second.

Examples:
$$(d + 3)(d + 4) = d^2 + 4d + 3d + 12$$
$$= d^2 + 7d + 12$$
$$(2x^2 - 3y)(3x - 4t) = 6x^3 - 8tx^2 - 9xy + 12ty$$

DON'T forget to do all four multiplications.

DO try using FOIL, standing for First, Outside, Inside, Last.

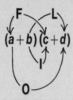

DON'T let that old devil minus lead you astray.

DO take extra care every time you see a minus sign.

B

1 Simplify these.

   a $4(s-2t)$ _____   **b** $4-5(w-3e)$ _____   **c** $a-a(b+c)$ _____

2 Simplify these by multiplying out the brackets, then collecting like terms.

   a $2a-a(a-3)$ _____   **b** $4a-(2a-a^2)$ _____

   c $5-4(a-4e)$ _____   **d** $a(a+5)+a(a-6)$ _____

3 Simplify these.

   a $(x-3)(x-5)$ _____   **b** $(x-1)(x+7)$ _____

   c $(e-f)(e+f)$ _____   **d** $(2a+3b)(2a-3b)$ _____

Common factors

- The expression $3a+6b$ has a **common factor** of 3 so $3a+6b$ can be factorised into $3(a+2b)$.

Examples:

$4x^2y-2x = 2x(2xy-1)$

$np^3+3p^2 = p^2(np+3)$

Always check your factorisation by multiplying it back out again.

C

Factorise these.

   a $3x+6$ _____   **b** $ab-ac$ _____

   c $2ab+4a^2$ _____   **d** $3a^2b-3ab$ _____

   e $2\pi r^2+\pi rl$ _____   **f** $2\pi r^2+2\pi rh$ _____

Transforming formulae or change of subject

This is tricky if you are not sure about algebraic rules, but the inverse (arrow) method may help.

The inverse method cannot be used if the new subject appears more than once in the formula.

Example:
Make n the subject of $r = 3n - u$.

Start with the subject letter, then gradually build up the right-hand side of the formula.

$$n \xrightarrow{\times 3} 3n \xrightarrow{-u} 3n - u$$

You know that $3n - u = r$, so you now work backwards using inverses (see Section A4).

$$\frac{r+u}{3} \xleftarrow{\div 3} r + u \xleftarrow{+u} r \leftarrow \textbf{Start here!}$$

Answer: $n = \dfrac{r+u}{3}$

DO	make sure you start with the *new* subject letter.
DO	be careful with self-inverses like 'taken from' and 'divided into'.

Example:
Make t the subject of $s = 3(a - t) + g$.

$$t \xrightarrow{-\text{from } a} a - t \xrightarrow{\times 3} 3(a-t) \xrightarrow{+g} 3(a-t)+g$$
$$\downarrow$$
$$a - \frac{s-g}{3} \xleftarrow{-\text{from } a} \frac{s-g}{3} \xleftarrow{\div 3} s - g \xleftarrow{-g} s$$

Answer: $t = a - \dfrac{s-g}{3}$

You can do these questions by changing sides as if you were solving an equation; if the subject letter appears twice you **must** use this method. The aim is to isolate the subject letter as a positive term on one side of the equals sign.

Be careful with signs and brackets.

Example:
Make g the subject of $h = k - 3(g + e)$.

Remove the bracket. $\qquad h = k - 3g - 3e$

Add $3g$ to both sides to make the g term positive.

$$h + 3g = k - 3e$$

Subtract h from both sides. $\quad 3g = k - 3e - h$

Divide both sides by 3. $\qquad g = \dfrac{k - 3e - h}{3}$

As we said, this is tricky!

D

1 Given that $a = 3x - 2gh$ make each of these the subject.
 a x **b** g

$x = \rule{2cm}{0.4pt}$ $g = \rule{2cm}{0.4pt}$

2 Make s the subject of $x = 3(s+t)+v$.

$s = \rule{2cm}{0.4pt}$

3 $V = \frac{4}{3}\pi r^3$ is the formula for the volume of a sphere.
 Write a formula to calculate the radius of a sphere, given the required volume.

$r = \rule{2cm}{0.4pt}$

4 The time of swing of a pendulum l metres long is given by the formula $t = 2\pi \sqrt{\dfrac{l}{g}}$
 seconds, where g is the acceleration due to gravity in metres per second per
 second.
 Write a formula to calculate g for a pendulum l metres long, if the time of swing is
 t seconds.

$g = \rule{2cm}{0.4pt}$

A3 ● SOLVING EQUATIONS

Solving linear equations

• Equations with just one letter term are best solved by inspection.

Example:

Find h when $3h + 8 = 5$.

Think: When $3h$ is added to 8 it gives 5.

Think: $-3 + 8 = 5$ Write: $3h = -3$

Think: If $3h$ is equal to -3 then h must be $\frac{1}{3}$ of -3.

               Write: $h = -3 \div 3 = -1$

It is best to remove the smaller letter term (the one further down the number line).

• Equations with two letter terms, one on each side of the equals sign, must have one of the letter terms removed. Do this by adding or subtracting the same term on both sides of the equals sign.

Example:

$4n - 4 = 8 - 6n$

Add $6n$ to both sides. The equation will still be in balance, but the $-6n$ will vanish.

$10n - 4 = 8$

Think: $12 - 4 = 8$ Write: $10n = 12$

Think: n must be $\frac{1}{10}$ of 12   Write: $n = 12 \div 10 = 1.2$

A

1 Solve these to find the value of the letter.

  a $3d - 1 = 5$ **b** $4 - 2a = 4$

  c $8 + 3a = 2$ **d** $9 = 4 - 2a$

  e $3f + 27 = 8$

2 Solve these.

  a $5 + x = 2x - 1$ **b** $9 + 6a = 3 + 4a$

  c $2a - 8 = 5a - 32$ **d** $a + 3 = 3a + 11$

  e $4a + 7 - a = 3 + 6a - 23$ **f** $7 + 5a - 1 = 3a + 24 - 4a$

  g $3 - 5k = 2k - 5 + k$

Solving polynomials by trial and improvement

- Polynomials can be solved by estimating an answer, testing to see how near you are, then making a better estimate, and so on.
- Polynomial equations often have several solutions but in a test you will probably only have to find one.

> A polynomial is an equation with at least one letter term of index 2 (a **quadratic**) or higher.

Example:

Solve $n^3 - 2n = 9$ correct to two decimal places.

Try $n = 2$

$n = 2$ gives $2^3 - (2 \times 2) = 4$ Too small!

$n = 3$ gives $3^3 - (2 \times 3) = 21$ Too big!

Now we home in on the answer.

$n = 2.5 \rightarrow 10.625$ Too big.

$n = 2.3 \rightarrow 7.567$ Too small.

$n = 2.45 \rightarrow 9.806$ Too big.

$n = 2.41 \rightarrow 9.178$ Bit too big.

$n = 2.39 \rightarrow 8.872$ Bit too small.

$n = 2.395 \rightarrow 8.948$ Bit too small.

$n = 2.399 \rightarrow 9.009$ Close enough.

One answer is 2.40 correct to two decimal places.

> Many polynomials have no exact answer. You will be told how accurate your answer needs to be.

> Why start with $n = 2$? Experience! Choosing $n = 10$, say, would be silly, as 10^3 is 1000, yet $n^3 - 2n$ only equals 9!

> Use a calculator!

DON'T give your closest approximation as the answer. The answer to the above example is not 9.009!

B

1 Find two solutions to each equation.

a $5x - x^2 = 6$

$x =$ _____ or _____

b $2a^2 - a = 3$

$a =$ _____ or _____

c $(3x + 1)(2x + 3) = 0$

$x =$ _____ or _____

2 Solve $x^3 - 2x^2 = 0$.

$x =$ _____ or _____

3 Find two approximate solutions to $a^2 - 3a - 6 = 0$.

$a =$ _____ or _____

Solving simultaneous equations

- With two different letters you need two equations.
- **Substitution method**
  Use when one equation is in the form 'letter equals', or $x = \ldots$.

Example:

Find x and y when $y = 3x - 4$ and $x - 2y = 5$.

As we know that $y = 3x - 4$ we can rewrite the second equation just using x.

$x - 2(3x - 4) = 5$

Now we can solve this.

$x - 6x + 8 = 5 \rightarrow -5x + 8 = 5 \rightarrow -5x = -3$

So $x = -3 \div -5 = 0.6$.

And as $y = 3x - 4$ we see that $y = 1.8 - 4 = -2.2$.

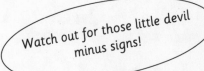

Watch out for those little devil minus signs!

- **Elimination method**
  This is the best method to use when neither equation is given in the 'letter equals' form.

You could make one letter the subject of one of the equations and use the substitution method instead.

Example:

Given that $3x - 2n = 6$ and that $2x + 2n = 9$ find x and n.

If we add these together, each side will still equal the other side, but because $-2n$ plus $2n$ equals zero we shall eliminate the n terms.

$$
\begin{array}{ll}
3x - 2n = & 6 \\
\underline{2x + 2n = } & 9 \qquad \text{Add} \\
5x \quad\; = 15 \rightarrow x = 3.
\end{array}
$$

Now use $3x - 2n = 6$ to find n.

$3x - 2n = 6 \rightarrow 9 - 2n = 6 \rightarrow n = 1.5$

Answer: $x = 3, n = 1.5$

The correct term for the 3 in 3r is **coefficient**.

- If **neither** pair of letter terms has the same number we multiply one or both of the equations to make one letter term the same.

When possible, avoid minus sign devils by changing the terms that will be eliminated when they are added.

Example:

Given that $3r - 2t = 3$ and that $4r - 5t = 6$, find r and t.

We could make $3r$ and $4r$ both into $12r$ or $2t$ and $5t$ both into $10t$. Free choice! Choose $12r$.

Multiply everything in the first equation by 4.

Multiply everything in the second equation by 3.

$$
\begin{array}{ll}
3r - 2t = 3 \rightarrow 12r - \;\,8t = 12 \\
\underline{4r - 5t = 6 \rightarrow 12r - 15t = 18} \qquad \text{Subtract} \\
\qquad\qquad\qquad\quad 7t = -6 \\
\qquad\qquad\qquad\quad\; t = -\tfrac{6}{7}
\end{array}
$$

Substituting in $3r - 2t = 3$ gives $r = \tfrac{3}{7}$.

Answer: $t = -\tfrac{6}{7}, r = \tfrac{3}{7}$

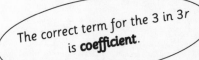

You can also solve simultaneous equations by drawing them as straight line graphs and finding where they cross.

C

1 Solve these simultaneously.

a $4x + y = 13$ and $y = x - 2$

$x = $ _____ $y = $ _____

b $y = x - 2$ and $x + y = 2$

$x = $ _____ $y = $ _____

c $3a - 2b = 8$ and $b = 2a - 5$

$a = $ _____ $b = $ _____

d $e = 2f - 7$ and $2f - 3e = 9$

$e = $ _____ $f = $ _____

2 Solve these simultaneously.

a $4x - 2y = 14$ and $x + 2y = 1$

$x = $ _____ $y = $ _____

b $2x + 3y = 5$ and $4x + 3y = 1$

$x = $ _____ $y = $ _____

c $3c - 5d = 11$ and $2c + 3d = 1$

$c = $ _____ $d = $ _____

d $9g + 2h = -7$ and $12g - 7h = 10$

$g = $ _____ $h = $ _____

A4 ● NUMBER PATTERNS

Explaining sequences

You must be able to use mathematical words to explain how a sequence has been formed, and how you can work out the next term.

Example:

Find the next term in the sequence 4, 7, 13, 25, 49, . . .

Each new term is found by doubling the last one, then subtracting 1.

The next term will be $2 \times 49 - 1 = 97$

Make sure you know the meaning of multiple, factor, prime, reciprocal, square and square root, cube and cube root. See the glossary and index.

Generating sequences

- A **sequence** is generated from an **nth term** such as $2n + 1$.
- To generate the sequence you replace the n by 1 for the 1st term, by 2 for the 2nd, and so on.
  For the nth term $2n + 1$ the sequence is

$$(2 \times 1) + 1, (2 \times 2) + 1, (2 \times 3) + 1, (2 \times 4) + 1, \ldots$$

or 3, 5, 7, 9, . . . , so the sequence $2n + 1$ generates odd numbers.

A sequence is a set of numbers linked by a rule.

Using a computer

- A spreadsheet is useful for generating sequences, as the rule can be put in the first cell, and the spreadsheet will then alter it in each following cell and print the sequence. As spreadsheets use different methods to set up the information you will need to learn to use a particular one yourself.
- It is even easier to generate a sequence using the BASIC programming language.

Example:
```
10 FOR N = 1 TO 10
20 PRINT 2 * N − 1
30 NEXT
```

This uses a FOR/NEXT loop to print the first ten terms of the sequence with nth term $2n - 1$.

A computer uses $2 * n$ for $2n$, $n/2$ for $n \div 2$ and $n \wedge 2$ for n^2

Standard sequence patterns

Making up nth terms and seeing what sequences you get will help you to find nth terms for given sequences.
These are the most likely ones you will meet.

Type: arithmetic: $an + b$, e.g. $4n$, $5n + 1$, $2n - 3$
Example: 4, 6, 8, 10, 12, . . .

Type: geometric: a^n or ar^{n-1}, e.g. 2^n, $2 \times 3^{n-1}$
Example: 6, 12, 24, 48, 96, . . .

Type: squares, n^2; cubes n^3
Examples: 1, 4, 9, 16, 25, . . . and 1, 8, 27, 64, 125, . . .

Type: triangular numbers, nth term $\frac{1}{2}n(n + 1)$
Triangular numbers start: 1, 3, 6, 10, 15, 21, 28, 36, . . .

Type: Fibonacci, 1, 1, 2, 3, 5, 8 . . . nth term too complex for this book.

Write out the first few terms of these sequences, and others like them.

Triangular numbers can be represented by triangles of dots.

ALGEBRA

Common difference method

- If whenever you subtract one term from the one before it the answer is the same (a **common difference**), you know the nth term is of the form $an+b$.

  Further, a will be the common difference and $a+b$ will be the first term.

Example:

5		7		9		11		13	
	2		2		2		2		the common difference is 2

$a = 2$, and $a+b = 5$, so $b = 3$.

The nth term is $2n+3$.

- If the first line does not give a common difference, try the next line. If that does, the nth term is an^2+bn+c where $2a$ is the common difference, $3a+b$ is the first difference in line one, and $a+b+c$ is the first number in the sequence.

Example:

4		8		14		22		32		44
	4		6		8		10		12	
		2		2		2		2		2

$2a = 2$, so $a = 1$
$3a+b = 4$, so $b = 1$
$a+b+c = 4$ so $c = 2$

The nth term is n^2+n+2.

A

1 Explain in words **(i)** how to find the next term in the sequence and, **(ii)** what it is.

a $2, 4, 6, 8, 10, \ldots$

b $1, 3, 6, 10, 15, 21, \ldots$

c $1, 4, 9, 16, 25, \ldots$

d $1, 8, 27, 64, 125, \ldots$

e $5, 3, 2, 1.5, 1.25, \ldots$

f $\frac{1}{7}, \frac{1}{14}, \frac{1}{21}, \frac{1}{28}, \frac{1}{35}, \ldots$

2 Write the first five terms of the sequences with the following nth terms.

a $3n-2$
b $\frac{1}{2}n(n+1)$
c 10^{n-1}

3 Find the nth term of each of these sequences.

a $7, 9, 11, 13, 15, \ldots$ **b** $17, 14, 11, 8, 5, \ldots$ **c** $3, 7, 13, 21, 31, \ldots$

nth term_____ nth term_____ nth term_____

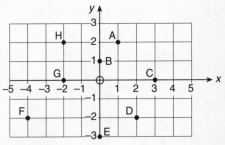

Figure A5:1

A5 ● CARTESIAN GRAPHS

Co-ordinates

• Co-ordinates fix the position of points on the grid.
  In Figure A5:1 A is at (1,2), B is at (0,1) and G is at (−2,0).

DON'T	get the numbers the wrong way round.
DON'T	get the axes the wrong way round.
DO	remember *x* (a-cross) comes before *y* (up and down).

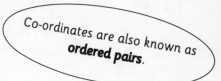

Co-ordinates are also known as **ordered pairs**.

Mappings

• A mapping gives a rule for changing a set of values called the **domain** into another set called the **range**.

Be very careful to start with 0 for points on the *y*-axis.

Example:
Given the mapping $x \to 2x - 1$ and the domain $\{-2, 0, 2, 4\}$, state the range then plot a graph of the function $f(x): x \to 2x - 1$.

Answer: The range is calculated by letting *x* equal −2, 0, 2 and 4 in the mapping.

When $x = -2$, $\quad 2x - 1 \to (2 \times -2) - 1 = -5$.
When $x = 0$, $\quad\quad 2x - 1 \to (2 \times 0) - 1 = -1$.

Similarly, $x = 2$ gives 3, and $x = 4$ gives 7.

The range is $\{-5, -1, 3, 7\}$.

The pairs of numbers in the domain and range give us co-ordinates which we can use as shown in Figure A5:2.

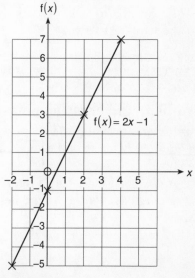

Figure A5:2

A

1 Given the mapping $x \to 4 - x$ find the range when the domain is $\{-3, -2, -1, 0, 1, 2, 3\}$.

Range _____

2 Draw a graph of the mapping $x \to 4 - x$.

3 Draw a graph for $f(x): x \to 2x + 1$ for *x* from −3 to +3.

Graphs of linear functions

- Equations of the family $y = mx + c$ where m and c are fixed (constant) numbers give straight line (or **linear**) graphs.

When $m = 0$ we get equations like $y = 3$, $y = 0$ and $y = -2$. When $y = 0$ we get equations like $x = 2$, $x = 0$ and $x = -1$. Figure A5:3 shows these six graphs.

All y values on $y = 3$ are 3, but the x values are all different.

Note that $y = 0$ is the x-axis and $x = 0$ is the y-axis.

To draw graphs of equations such as $y = 2x - 1$ and $y - 3x = 4$ we need to find the co-ordinates of three points on each line.

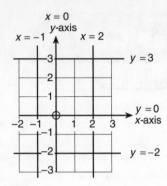

Figure A5:3

Example:

Draw graphs of **a** $y = 2x - 1$ and **b** $y - 3x = 4$ using x and y axes each labelled from -4 to 4.

a $y = 2x - 1$
Take $x = 2$, then $y = (2 \times 2) - 1 = 3$.
So $(2,3)$ lies on the line.
Similarly $x = -1$ gives $(-1, -3)$ and $x = 0$ gives $(0, -1)$.

b $y - 3x = 4$
Take $x = 0$, then $y = 4$, giving $(0,4)$.
Take $x = -1$ to give $(-1,1)$.
Take $x = -2$ to give $(-2, -2)$.

The resulting graphs are shown in Figure A5:4.

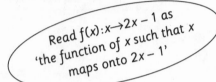

Read $f(x):x \to 2x - 1$ as 'the function of x such that x maps onto $2x - 1$'

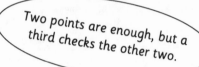

Two points are enough, but a third checks the other two.

Gradient and crossing point

A linear equation may always be written as $y = mx + c$. Then m represents the gradient or slope of the line, and c is the y value where the line crosses the y-axis.

The gradient is found from a right-angled triangle drawn under the line. A line sloping backwards (\) has a negative gradient, see Figures A5:5 and A5:6.

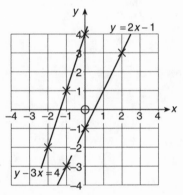

Figure A5:4

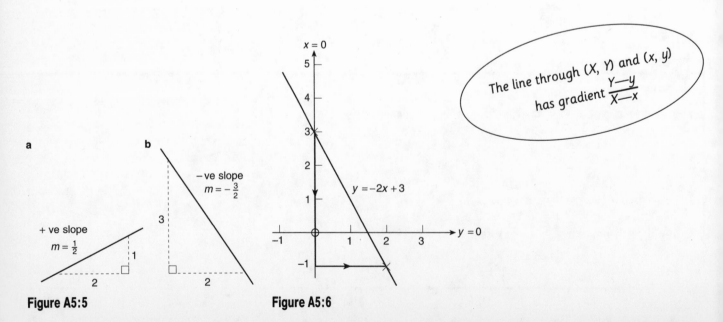

The line through (X, Y) and (x, y) has gradient $\dfrac{Y-y}{X-x}$

Figure A5:5

Figure A5:6

B

1 Draw a set of axes and label each of them from −6 to 6. Draw these graphs.
 a $y = x - 5$ **b** $y = 2x + 1$ **c** $y = 6 - x$ **d** $x + 3y = 6$

2 A straight line graph has gradient −1 and passes through (0,4). State the equation of the line.

———————————————————

3 By drawing a graph, or otherwise, find **(i)** the crossing point on the y-axis, and **(ii)** the gradient of each of these lines.
 a $y = 3x$ **b** $y = -4x + 7$
 (i) ————— **(ii)** —————   **(i)** ————— **(ii)** —————

4 By plotting on a grid, or otherwise, find the gradients of the lines through each of these pairs of points.
 a (3,4) and (4,6)   **b** (4,5) and (1,6)

   gradient —————   gradient —————

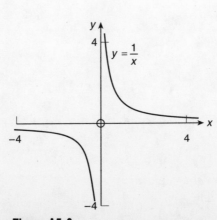

The path of a golf ball through the air is a parabola.

Form of quadratic, cubic, reciprocal and exponential graphs

You must know the rough shapes of these curved graphs. Use a computer or a graphical calculator to investigate their family shapes.

Quadratic (parabolic) Family $y = ax^2 + bx + c$
                          See Figure A5:7.

Cubic   Family $y = ax^3 + bx^2 + cx + d$
                          See Figure A5:8.

Reciprocal   Family $y = \dfrac{a}{x}$
                          See Figure A5:9.

Exponential   Family $y = a^x$
                          See Figure A5:10.

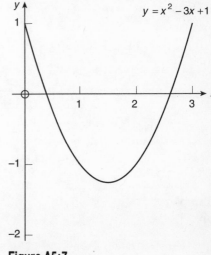

Figure A5:7

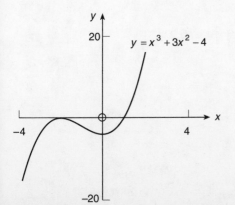

Figure A5:8

Figure A5:9

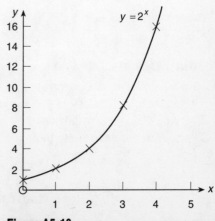

Figure A5:10

A6 ● INEQUALITIES

Reading inequality expressions

- $x < 2$ is read as 'x is less than 2'.
  $x > 3$ is read as 'x is more than 3'.
  $x \geqslant 5$ is read as 'x is more than or equal to 5'.
- When reading double inequalities read the letter first, then go left, back to the middle, then right.

Stating that $x \geq 5$ means 'x is not less than 5' is better English.

Example:
$4 \leqslant x < 7$ is 'x is more than or equal to 4 and x is less than 7'.

Stating that $4 \leq x < 7$ means 'x is less than 7 but not less than 4' is better English.

Solving inequalities

- Inequalities are like equations except that the letter has a range of values. If $2x = 6$ then x must be 3, but if $2x > 6$ ($2x$ is more than 6) then we only know that $x > 3$.
- Inequalities can usually, but not always, be solved as if they were equations. Always check by substituting one value in the solution range.

Example:
Solve $3x + 4 > 1$.

If $3x + 4 = 1$, then $3x = -3$ giving $x = -1$.

So try the inequality solution $x > -1$.

Test this by, say, letting $x = 1$.

$3 \times 1 + 4 = 7$, which is more than 1, so all is well.

When $x = -2$
$-2x = -2 \times -2 = +4$

In the next example the check is vital, as the inequality sign has to be turned round to give the correct answer.

Example:
Solve $5 - 2x < 3$.

Thinking of it as $5 - 2x = 3$ we get $x = 1$.

But $x < 1$ is not the answer, as if x was -2, then $5 - 2x$ would be 9.

The correct answer is $x > 1$. Test this with $x = 4$.

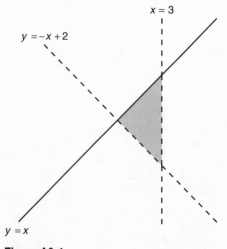

Figure A6:1

Inequalities on a graph

Figure A6:1 shows the graphs of $x = 3$, $y = -x + 2$ and $y = x$.
  The value of x gets less as you move to the left.
  The value of y gets greater as you move up, and less as you move down.
  The region between these lines is:

$$x < 3 \qquad \text{(on the left of the line } x = 3\text{)}$$
$$y \leqslant x \qquad \text{(on or below the line } y = x\text{)}$$
$$y > -x + 2 \qquad \text{(above the line } y = -x + 2\text{)}.$$

We can write this as $\{(x,y): x < 3; -x + 2 < y \leqslant x\}$.

The region does not include the dotted line, so use $x < 3$ not $x \leq 3$.

$\{(x,y): \dots \}$ means the set of points on a graph.

A

1 Rewrite each of these using inequality signs.
  a n is more than 16 but less than 18. _____
  b w is less than 65 but not less than 21. _____
  c p is not more than 16 and not less than 5. _____

2 Solve these.
  a $3x - 5 > 16$ **b** $4 - x > 1$

                                x _____ x _____

  c $\dfrac{30}{x} \leqslant 6$ **d** $5 - 3x \geqslant 8$

                                x _____ x _____

3 Draw a set of axes, each labelled from -4 to 4, and indicate the region
  $\{(x, y): -3 < y < 2; y < x\}$.

4 Draw a set of axes, each labelled from -4 to 4, and indicate the region
  $\{(x, y): 0 < x < 2; 0 < y < \frac{1}{2}x + 1\}$.

S1 ● THE LANGUAGE OF SHAPE

Measuring angles

- Angles are measured by how much of a turn they represent (Figure S1:1).

> 360° is a full turn
> 180° is a straight line
> 90° is a right angle

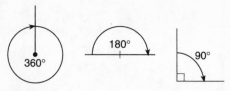

Figure S1:1

- Angles are measured using a protractor.
  In Figure S1:2 the protractor shows the angle is 120°.

> Note the special symbol for a right angle.

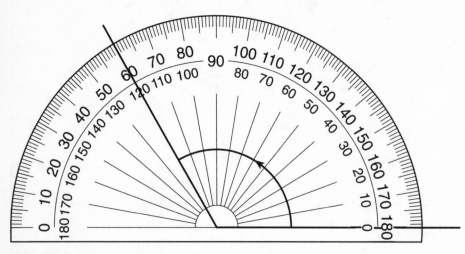

Figure S1:2

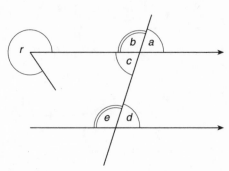

Figure S1:3

DON'T	read the wrong scale; the angle in Figure S1:2 is not 60°.
DO	read from the 0 which is on the angle line.
DO	always estimate your answer first, then measure.

> The arrows on the two lines mean that they are parallel.

Special kinds of angle

- **Angles named by their size**
  In Figure S1:3:

> An estimate of more than 90° or less than 90° is accurate enough.

> angle *a* is acute (less than 90°)
> angle *b* is obtuse (between 90° and 180°)
> angle *r* is reflex (more than 180°)

- **Angles where two straight lines meet**
  In Figure S1:3:

> Adjacent means 'next to each other'.

> $a + b = 180°$ (adjacent angles on a straight line)
>
> $a = c$ (vertically opposite angles)

> Two angles that make 180° are **supplementary**.

- **Angles between parallel lines**
  In Figure S1:3:

> Think of 'alternate' as meaning on opposite sides.

> $a = d$ (corresponding angles between parallel lines)
> $c = d$ (alternate angles between parallel lines)
>
> $c + e = 180°$ (allied angles between parallel lines)

> Allied means joined together. Angles like these are also called **'interior'** or **'conjoining'**.

A

1 a In Figure S1:4, measure angles

   (i) f _____ °   **(ii)** g _____ °   **(iii)** c _____ °

  b What kind of angles are **(i)** e **(ii)** h?   e _____   h _____

  c Name two pairs of:

   (i) adjacent angles on a straight line _____

   (ii) alternate angles _____

   (iii) vertically opposite angles _____

   (iv) corresponding angles _____

   (v) allied angles. _____

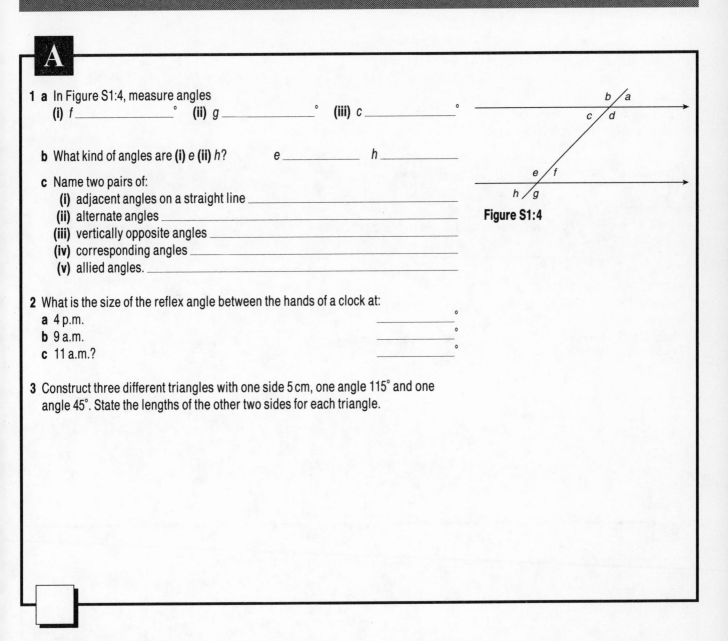

Figure S1:4

2 What is the size of the reflex angle between the hands of a clock at:

  a 4 p.m.   _____ °

  b 9 a.m.   _____ °

  c 11 a.m.?   _____ °

3 Construct three different triangles with one side 5 cm, one angle 115° and one angle 45°. State the lengths of the other two sides for each triangle.

Plane figures

- **Regular** figures can fit all their vertices on a circle. They have all sides and all angles the same size.
- A **polygon** is a many-sided shape (see Section S2).
- Learn the names of the parts of a circle shown in Figure S1:5.

A plane figure has only two dimensions, like a triangle.

A vertex (plural vertices) is a corner of a shape.

Figure S1:5

Solids

• Family names of solids

Prisms are the same shape all through their length.

Examples:

cube, cuboid, unsharpened pencil, cylinder

Pyramids are built on a base with sides rising to a point.

Examples:

Egyptian pyramid (square base), tetrahedron (triangular base),
cone (circular base)

Spheres are round solid shapes, like tennis balls.
Figure S1:6 shows a cube of Oxo, a sphere used in golf, a cuboid of tile
cement and a cylinder of Ideal milk.
Figure S1:7 shows a cone, a hexagonal prism and a tetrahedron.

*In mathematics, **solid** means three-dimensional. A mathematical solid can be hollow!*

Figure S1:6

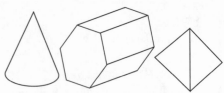

Figure S1:7

Learn all these names and their spellings.

B

1 Name the solids for which the plans and elevations are drawn in Figure S1:8.

a _____ b _____ c _____

d _____ e _____ f _____

g _____

A plan is looking from above.

An elevation is looking from in front.

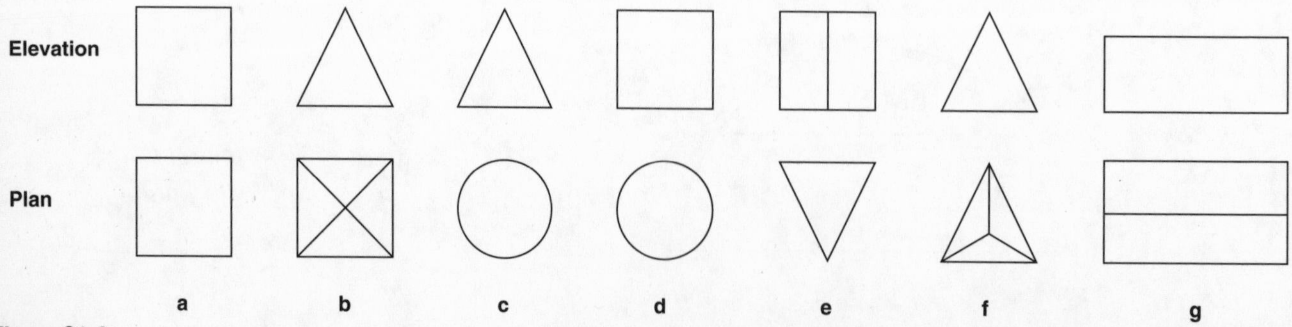

Elevation

Plan

a   b   c   d   e   f   g

Figure S1:8

S2 ● POLYGONS

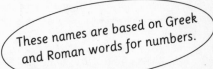

These names are based on Greek and Roman words for numbers.

Special names

- Polygons are many-sided figures.
- Regular polygons have equal sides **and** equal angles.
- **Polygon names**

3 triangle	4 quadrilateral	5 pentagon
6 hexagon	7 heptagon	8 octagon
9 nonagon	10 decagon	12 dodecagon

> **DON'T** draw a polygon regular unless you KNOW it is regular.
>
> **DO** remember that unless a polygon has all sides equal AND all angles equal you cannot call it regular.

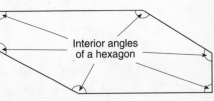

Interior angles of a hexagon

Figure S2:1

Angle sums

- **Interior angles**

    Figure S2:1 shows the interior angles of a hexagon.
    The formula to calculate the sum of the interior angles of polygons is

$$(n-2) \times 180°$$

where n is the number of sides.

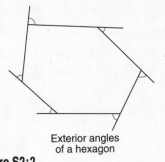

Exterior angles of a hexagon

Figure S2:2

Examples:

The angle sum of a triangle is $(3-2) \times 180° = 180°$

The angle sum of a pentagon is $(5-2) \times 180° = 540°$

- **Exterior angles**

    Figure S2:2 shows the exterior angles of a hexagon.
    The exterior angle sum of any polygon is 360°. It does not change however many sides it has.

scalene   isosceles   equilateral

Figure S2:3

Special triangles

Figure S2:3 shows the special names for triangles.
- **Scalene:** no equal sides
- **Isosceles:** two equal sides and angles
- **Equilateral:** all sides equal and all angles 60°

The special facts about their diagonals need not be learnt as you can always sketch the figure and check!

Special quadrilaterals

- Figure S2:4 shows the special kinds of quadrilateral.
- Each figure after the trapezium is a special sort of the figure drawn before it.

Trapezium   Isosceles trapezium (equal diagonals)

Kite

Examples:

A parallelogram is an isosceles trapezium with the two equal sides parallel.

A square is a rectangle with four equal sides.

Parallelogram   Rhombus

Tessellation

A tessellation is formed by a set of shapes which cover area, without leaving any gaps. All triangles and quadrilaterals tessellate with themselves. Other shapes may combine together, for example, regular octagons with squares. Investigate!

Rectangle (equal diagonals)   Square (equal diagonals)

Figure S2:4

A

1 Draw an example of the following if possible. If it is not possible say why not.
   a a right-angled scalene triangle
   b an isosceles right-angled triangle
   c an equilateral right-angled triangle

2 Find one fact about the set of shapes {C, F, G, H} in Figure S2:5 that makes them different from all the others.

_____

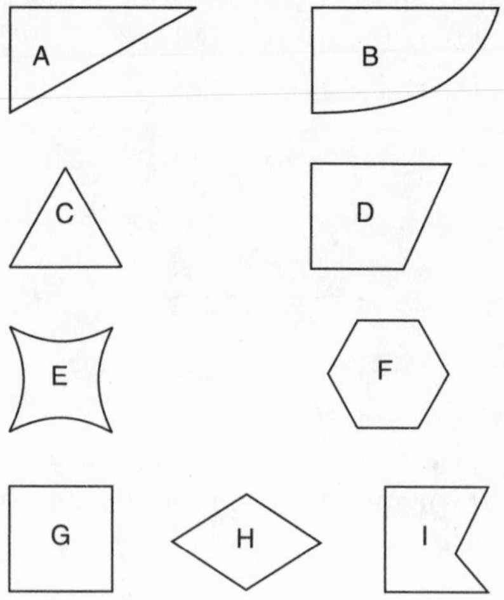

3 Give the usual name for:
   a a regular quadrilateral _____
   b an infinite-sided polygon. _____

4 Find the size of one exterior angle in a 20-sided regular polygon.

_____°

Figure S2:5

5 Which of the following cannot be the size of the interior angle of a regular polygon? Why not?
   a 90° b 60° c 140° d 72° e 160°

_____ cannot be, because _____
_____.

6 The exterior and interior angles of a regular polygon are in the ratio 2:13. How many sides has the polygon?

_____ sides

7 Find properties of a non-isosceles trapezium and an isosceles trapezium that are true about:
   a both of them _____
_____

   b only one of them. _____
_____

8 Amy has two 8 cm and two 5 cm straws. What quadrilaterals could she make if she joins their ends?

_____

9 In which quadrilaterals do the diagonals cross at 90°?

_____

S3 ● SYMMETRY

Lines of symmetry

- A **line of symmetry** divides a shape into two **congruent** sections, one half being a reflection of the other.
  Figure S3:1 shows the lines of symmetry of a square and an equilateral triangle.

DON'T	give a parallelogram any lines of symmetry.
DON'T	give a rectangle more than two lines of symmetry.
DO	cut out figures and try to fold them exactly in half to find lines of symmetry.

Rotational symmetry

- The **order** of rotational symmetry is the number of times a shape will fit into its tracing in one full rotation.
  In Figure S3:1, the square is of order 4, the equilateral triangle is of order 3, and the parallelogram is of order 2.
- All shapes fit once into their tracing, but examiners may not count this and so expect the answer 'No' to a question such as 'Does an isosceles trapezium have rotational symmetry?'

Don't write 'axes of symmetry'; only solids have these.

All **regular** polygons have the same number of lines of symmetry as sides.

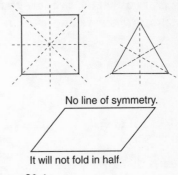

No line of symmetry.

It will not fold in half.

Figure S3:1

An even order of rotational symmetry gives a shape **point symmetry**.

All **regular** polygons have the same order of rotational symmetry as sides.

A

1 Draw examples of the following shapes on a piece of paper, then for each
  (i) draw all its lines of symmetry
  (ii) state its order of rotational symmetry
  (iii) cut out the shapes and check your answer to **(i)** by folding and **(ii)** by turning.
  a isosceles triangle   **b** equilateral triangle
  c kite   **d** right-angled trapezium
  e isosceles trapezium   **f** parallelogram
  g rhombus   **h** rectangle
  i square   **j** regular hexagon

(ii) Order of rotational symmetry

Shape	a	b	c	d	e	f	g	h	i	j
Lines of symmetry										
Order of rotational symmetry										

2 Draw a hexagon that has only two lines of symmetry and rotational symmetry of order 2.

Planes of symmetry

- **Planes of symmetry** cut a solid into two congruent pieces, each half being a mirror image of the other.
  Figure S3:2 shows two of the planes of symmetry of a cuboid for which the top face is a square.

Use a ball of Plasticene to make some regular solids and check it for yourself.

Axes of symmetry

- If you can rotate a solid about an axis so that it looks identical more than once during a full revolution, the imaginary rods about which it turns are called the **axes of symmetry**.
  Figure S3:3 shows one of the axes of symmetry, UZ, of a cuboid.

It helps greatly if you can handle the solids you need to know about.

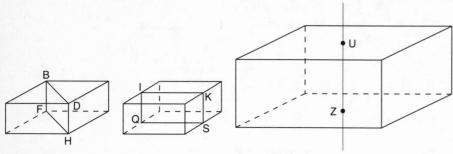

Figure S3:2   **Figure S3:3**

Symmetry number

- The number of different ways a solid can be placed into a mould of itself is its **symmetry number**.
  A cube has symmetry number 24, as each of the six faces could be on top and be set in four ways, depending which edge is nearest you.

B

1 Using modelling clay or potatoes, make various solids and investigate their symmetries. Study, at least, a cuboid, a cube, a tetrahedron, a square-based pyramid and an equilateral-triangular prism.

S4 ● SPECIFYING LOCATION

Cardinal point bearings

- Figure S4:1 shows the 16 **cardinal points** of the compass. The magnetised needle always points north.
- Other directions are given as turns from north and south towards east and west.
  Figure S4:2 shows a journey which started out on bearing N50°E, then turned to bearing N60°W.

> On a map north is usually shown going up the page.

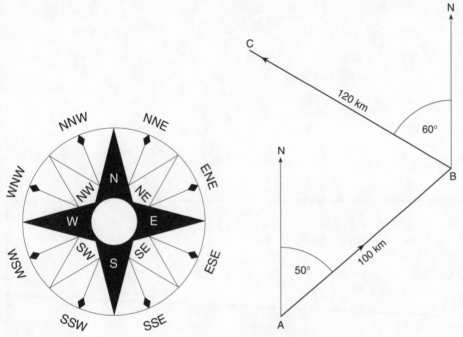

Figure S4:1   Figure S4:2

Three-figure bearings

- In the three-figure bearing system, directions are measured clockwise from north, so NE becomes 045° and NW become 315°.
  Figure S4:3 shows a journey which started out on a bearing of 060°, then turned to 300°.

> Three-figure bearings must always have three figures, so sometimes a zero is put at the front, as in 045°.

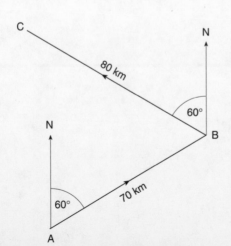

> Where did the 300° come from?

Figure S4:3

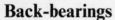

Back-bearings

- To find out where you are on a map, find the compass bearings of two objects you can identify on the map, then calculate your bearing (the **back-bearing**) from each object.

Example:
If John sees Molly on a bearing of 150°, Molly sees John on a back-bearing of 330° (Figure S4:4).

- To calculate a back-bearing, add on 180°, then, if the answer is more than 360°, take 360° away from your answer.

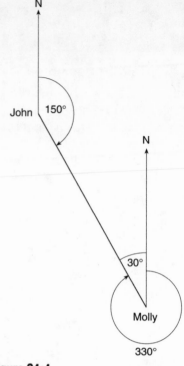

Figure S4:4

A

1 Where the following bearings are cardinal, write the three-figure equivalent, and vice versa.

a NW _____ **b** 135° _____ **c** 270° _____
d SW _____ **e** N15°E _____ **f** S25°W _____
g 190° _____ **h** 300° _____ **i** 265° _____

2 Two beacons, A and B, are on bearings 235° and 82° from an aeroplane. Find the bearings of the aeroplane from the beacons.

A _____° B _____°

3 Alan walks 4 km on bearing 120°, then 6 km on bearing 200° and finally 5 km NE. What is the bearing of his starting point, from his final position, and how far away is it?

_____° _____ km

S5 ● CONSTRUCTING SHAPES

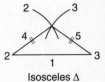

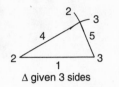

2-D

You need: a ruler, a protractor and a pair of compasses.

You should be able to use compasses to construct circles, triangles and quadrilaterals.

Figure S5:1 gives examples. The numbers are the steps in order.

3-D

Hollow 3-D shapes, such as boxes, can be made from nets.

Figure S5:2 shows some examples.

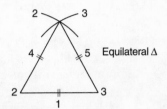

Figure S5:1

Note: Put a tab on every other edge.

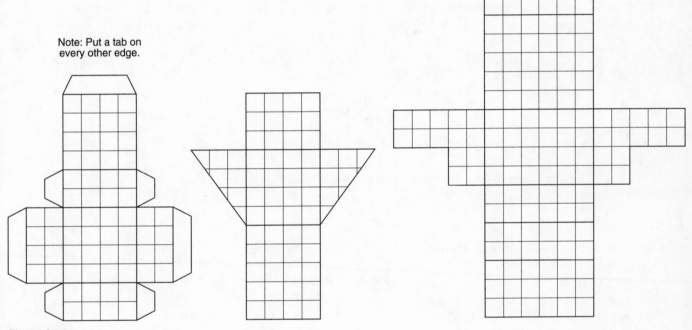

Figure S5:2

To make the models you need tabs to join the faces.

A

1 Construct the following shapes on plain paper as accurately as you can.
   a a square of side 4 cm surmounted by a semicircle
   b a rectangle of sides 4 cm and 6 cm with a circle through its four corners
   c an equilateral triangle of side 5 cm with a circle inside it touching all three sides
   d two different right-angled isosceles triangles with one side of length 50 mm
   e four different isosceles triangles each of which has a 40° angle and a 5 cm side

2 Construct accurately on plain paper three different nets for a tetrahedron which has all its sides 3 cm long. Cut out your nets and make the tetrahedron.

3 Construct some capital letter prisms.

4 Make a net of a lampshade.

Make tabs as large as possible to give strength and make it easy to glue.

Edges that join together must be the same length.

Do not let paper come near to a hot light-bulb!

S6 ● TRANSFORMATIONS

Reflection

- An **image** is the same distance behind a plane mirror as the **object** is in front.
- The line joining an object point and its image crosses the mirror at right angles (Figure S6:1).
- Your brain prefers a vertical mirror line.

> **DON'T** let examiners confuse you when they draw a sloping mirror line.
>
> **DO** just turn your paper round until the mirror line is upright!

- Describe a reflection as 'reflection in line AB' or 'reflection in the *x*-axis'. In Figure S6:2 triangle ABC is reflected in the line $y = -x$.

Rotation

- The object is turned about a point called the **centre of rotation**. You can use tracing paper. Fix the centre with the point of your compasses.
- The angle between a line on the object and its image is the same as the angle of rotation.
- To describe a rotation, state the angle turned and where the centre of rotation lies.

In Figure S6:3 triangle ABC has rotated through 90° clockwise about the centre of the grid, to give the image A′B′C′.

Enlargement

- In maths an object may be **enlarged** to make it smaller. (Well, you always thought maths was strange!)
  The amount by which lengths are changed is called the **scale factor**.
  Scale factor 2 makes all lengths twice as long.
  Scale factor $\frac{1}{2}$ makes all lengths $\frac{1}{2}$ as long.
- The object and image can be placed so that lines through corresponding object and image points meet at one point, called the **centre of the enlargement**.

Figures S6:4 and S6:5 show the object triangle ABC enlarged by scale factors 2 and $\frac{1}{2}$. Note how the distances of the points from the centre of enlargement change by the scale factor, so in Figure S6:4, $OC' = 2 \times OC$ and in Figure S6:5, $OC' = \frac{1}{2} \times OC$.

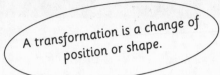
A transformation is a change of position or shape.

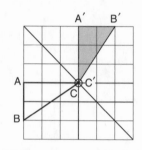

Figure S6:1

Figure S6:2

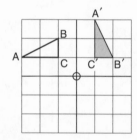

Figure S6:3

Angles stay the same size when enlarging.

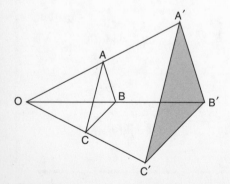

Figure S6:4

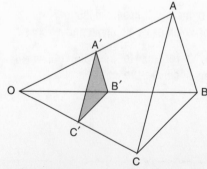

Figure S6:5

Translation

- A translation is a sliding movement.
- Translations are described by saying how far the move is left or right, and up or down.

This is sometimes written as a column matrix, stating how far the shape has moved right($+$) or left($-$), over how far it has moved up($+$) or down($-$).

In Figure S6:6, triangle X is translated to Z by a move of two squares right and four squares up, which can be written $\begin{pmatrix} 2 \\ 4 \end{pmatrix}$ and Z is translated to Y by moving four right and one down, or $\begin{pmatrix} 4 \\ -1 \end{pmatrix}$.

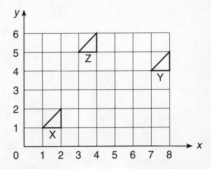

Figure S6:6

A

1 Study Figure S6:7.

  a Find a reflection and state the mirror line.

  _____

  b Find a rotation, stating the centre and the angle turned.

  _____

  c State the scale factor of the enlargement of

    (i) A to A_3 _____ **(ii)** A_3 to A_1. _____

  d Describe the translation of triangle A onto A_1.

  _____

2 Reflect each of the shapes in Figure S6:8 in the given mirror line, m.

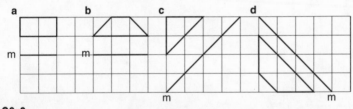
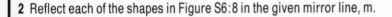

Figure S6:8

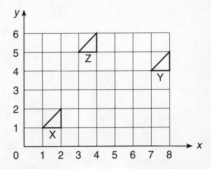

Figure S6:7

3 In Figure S6:9, draw the flags after rotations, about the marked centres, of **(i)** 180°, **(ii)** 90° clockwise, **(iii)** 270° clockwise.

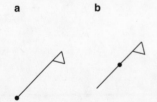
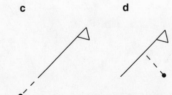

Figure S6:9

4 Trace the shapes in Figure S6:10. If the transformation is a rotation, mark the centre.

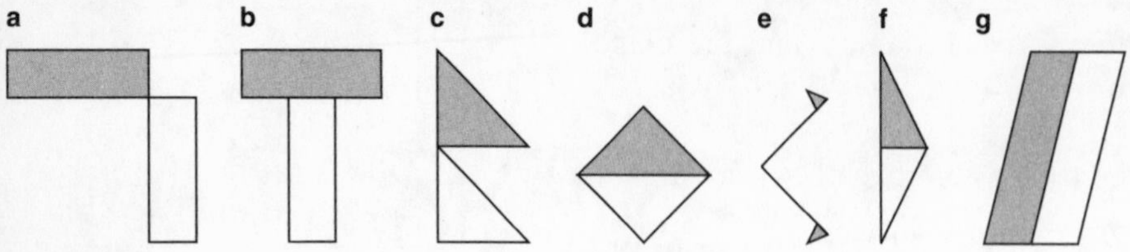

a   b   c   d   e   f   g

Figure S6:10

5 Describe the translation in Figure S6:6 (page 65) which translates:
  a X to Y _____
  b Y to X _____
  c Y to Z _____
  d Z to Y _____

6 **a** Draw a set of axes, *x* from 0 to 16, *y* from 0 to 10.
  b Draw the triangle with vertices at (4,4), (8,4) and (4,6).
  c Draw the image of the triangle after it has been enlarged by scale factor 2 from centre (3,3).
  d Draw the image of the triangle after it has been enlarged by scale factor ½ from centre the origin.
  e State the co-ordinates of the vertices of your two images.
    First image _____
    Second image _____

7 Enlarge the shape in Figure S6:11 by making each side twice as long.

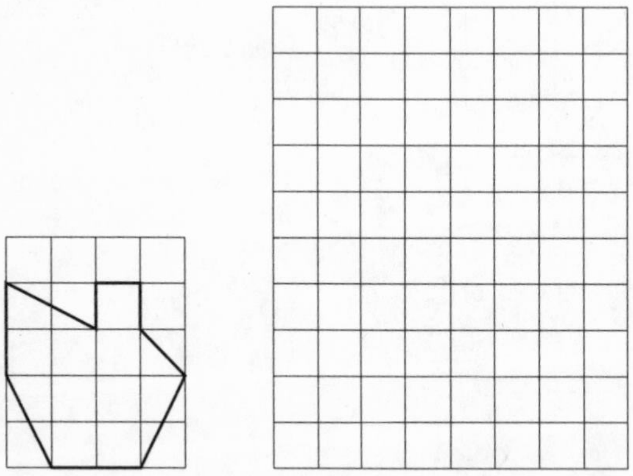

Figure S6:11

S7 ● COMPARING SHAPES

Congruence and similarity

- **Congruent** shapes are exactly the same shape and size.
- Two shapes are **similar** when one is an exact enlargement of the other (see Section S6).
- Families of regular shapes are always similar, e.g. equilateral triangles, squares, circles, cubes, spheres.
- Triangles are similar if their angles are the same **or** if their sides are in the same ratio.
- For other shapes to be similar their angles must be the same size **and** their corresponding sides must be in the same ratio.
- Study Figure S7:1.
  Rectangles A and B are similar. All sides are in the ratio 1:2.
  Rectangles A and C are not similar because the 3 side has become 9 (ratio 1:3) but the 4 side has become 15 (ratio 1:3.75).
  None of the rectangles is similar to a square, although all have angles of 90°.

Triangles are also similar if you know one angle is the same and the sides that make that angle are in the same ratio.

Corresponding means in the same position relative to the angles.

Calculating sides in similar figures

To calculate unknown sides you first find the scale factor of the enlargement. The sides you use must correspond. That is, both sides have the same angles at each end.

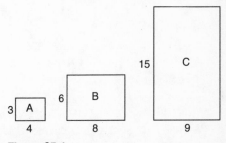

Figure S7:1

Example:

Calculate sides a and b in Figure S7:2.

As the 4 cm and 6 cm sides correspond, the scale factor is 4:6 or 2:3.

The sides of the larger triangle are $\frac{3}{2}$ times the sides of the smaller.

The sides of the smaller triangle are $\frac{2}{3}$ times the sides of the larger.

Answer:

$$a = \frac{2}{3} \times 5 = 3\frac{1}{3} \qquad\qquad b = \frac{3}{2} \times 2 = 3$$

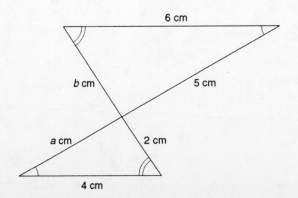

The triangles are similar as their angles are the same size.

Figure S7:2

A

1 Tick the true statement. All circles are:

A congruent _____ **B** similar _____ **C** neither of these. _____

2 Which shapes in Figure S7:3 are congruent?

_____

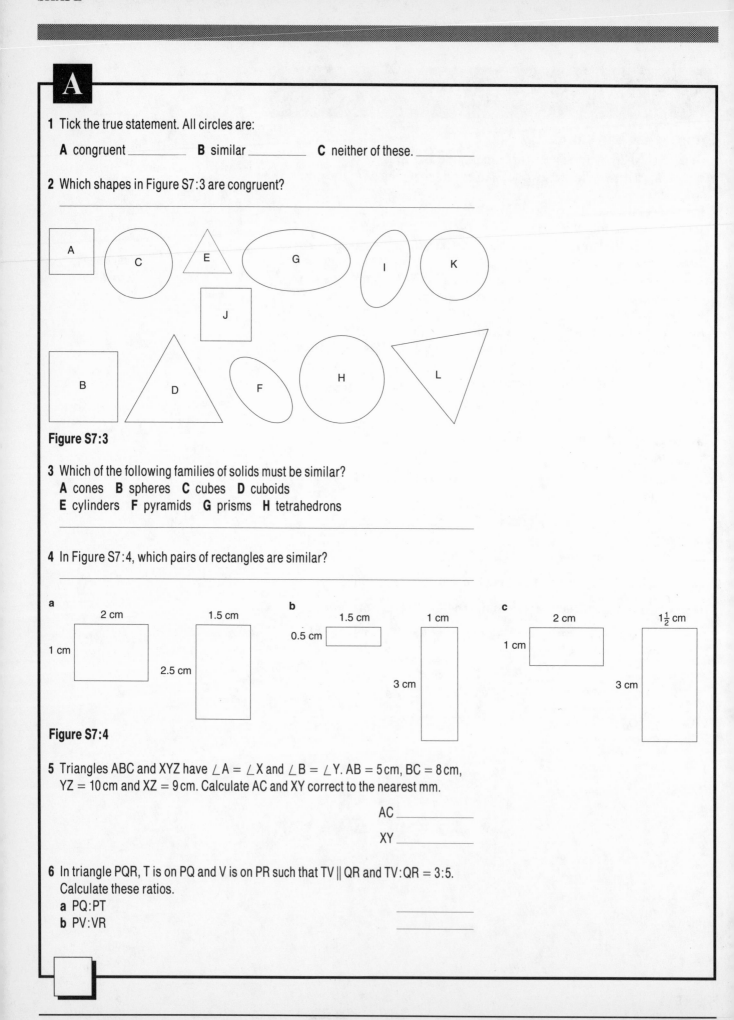

Figure S7:3

3 Which of the following families of solids must be similar?
   A cones **B** spheres **C** cubes **D** cuboids
   E cylinders **F** pyramids **G** prisms **H** tetrahedrons

_____

4 In Figure S7:4, which pairs of rectangles are similar?

_____

Figure S7:4

5 Triangles ABC and XYZ have $\angle$A = $\angle$X and $\angle$B = $\angle$Y. AB = 5 cm, BC = 8 cm,
   YZ = 10 cm and XZ = 9 cm. Calculate AC and XY correct to the nearest mm.

   AC _____

   XY _____

6 In triangle PQR, T is on PQ and V is on PR such that TV ∥ QR and TV:QR = 3:5.
   Calculate these ratios.
   a PQ:PT _____
   b PV:VR _____

S8 ● 2-D REPRESENTATION OF 3-D SHAPES

- Verticals on the solid must be vertical in the drawing.
- Parallel edges must be drawn as parallel lines in the drawing.

> In maths we do not use perspective to make parallel lines meet at the vanishing point.

Oblique projection

One face is drawn as it is seen straight on, and therefore keeps its true shape. The edges at right angles to this face go away at 45° and are drawn to half the scale of the front face (Figure S8:1).

> An oblique view is impossible in real life.

Isometric

Two faces at right angles are drawn with their edges going away at 30° to the horizontal. All vertical and 30° lines are drawn to the same scale (Figures S8:2 and S8:3).

> An isometric view is close to real-life, ignoring perspective.

Orthographic

The solid is drawn from three views, each exactly the true shape—from the front (the **elevation**), from the side (the **end-elevation**) and from above (the **plan**) (Figure S8:4).

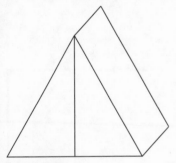

Figure S8:1

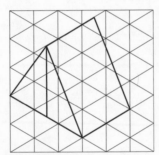

Figure S8:2

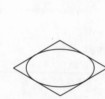

Figure S8:3

Figure S8:4

A

1. The block represented in Figure S8:5 is turned so that it stands on the face ABCD with AB nearest you. Draw views of the block in its new position in isometric, oblique and orthographic projections.

2. Draw a 3-D view of:
   a. a square-based pyramid
   b. a cylindrical can lying on its side.

3. Draw a plan view of each of the two objects in question **2**.

4. A house is a cuboid with a triangular prism on top. Sketch views of the house:
   a. seen from directly in front
   b. seen from one side
   c. seen from a hang-glider flying over it.

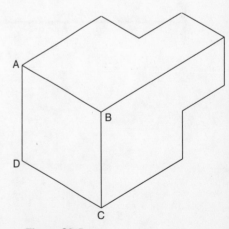

Figure S8:5

S9 ● LOGO

Using the LOGO language

- The LOGO computer language can be used to draw shapes.
- The main instructions are to turn RIGHT or LEFT a given number of degrees, and to move FORWARD a given distance.
- Instructions can be built into a REPEAT *n* . . . END loop where they are carried out *n* times.

Versions of LOGO differ, but all use the same basic idea.

Example:

Program   HEXAGON: REPEAT 6
              FORWARD 100
              RIGHT 60
              END

  or   TO HEXAGON
              REPEAT 6 [FORWARD 100 RIGHT 60]
              END

- Once you have saved this program you have added the instruction HEXAGON to your list of LOGO commands.

A

1 What shape will be drawn by these LOGO programs?

a FORWARD 52
  RIGHT 150
  FORWARD 30
  RIGHT 60
  FORWARD 30

b REPEAT 2
  FORWARD 50
  LEFT 150
  FORWARD 50
  LEFT 30
  END

M1 ● MEASURING

The metric system
- The metric system is based on the metre.
- Prefixes make the unit larger or smaller by powers of 10.
  You should know, at least:

> mega (a megatonne is one million tonnes)
> kilo   (a kilowatt is one thousand watts)
> hecto (a hectare is one hundred ares)
> centi   (a centilitre is one hundredth of a litre)
> milli   (a millimetre is one thousandth of a metre)
> micro (a microvolt is one millionth of a volt).

The metre was planned to be 2.5×10^{-8} of the equator, but someone miscalculated!

Metric units
- A **gram** is the weight of a cubic centimetre of water.
- A **litre** is the volume (or capacity) of a container that holds a kilogram of water.
- A **tonne** is 1000 kg.
- A **hectare** is the area of a square with sides 100 m long, that is 10 000 m².

Time
- The months alternate, long (31 days) and short (28, 29 or 30 days), except in the summer holidays.

Jan	Feb	Mar	Apr	May	Jun	Jul	Aug	Sep	Oct	Nov	Dec
31	28/29	31	30	31	30	31	31	30	31	30	31

- A normal year has 365 days. A **leap** year, when the last two digits divide exactly by 4, has 366.

After February anniversaries leap a day.

Changing from one metric unit to another
- The units figure of the measure you are converting must go into the correct column of the new measure.

Why is the year 2000 different from 1700, 1800 and 1900?

Example:
Convert 108.9 mm to metres.
1 mm is one thousandth of a metre, or 0.001 m.
8 mm is 0.008 m and 108.9 mm is 0.1089 m.
Answer: 108.9 mm = 0.1089 m

The 1 in 0.001 is put in the thousandths column.

Example:
Convert 15.076 km to metres.
 1 km is 1000 metres
15 km is 15 000 metres and 15.076 km is 15 076 m.
Answer: 15.076 km = 15 076 m

- When converting from one metric unit into another, extra zeros are sometimes needed at the beginning or end, but must never be written between the given figures.

Examples:
3.05 m → 3050 mm (extra zero needed at the end)
65 g → 0.065 kg (extra zeros at the beginning)

65 g is 'no thousand, no hundred and sixty-five grams'.

- When converting from mixed units to one unit you *may* need to insert zeros between the figures.

Example:
Change 15 m 23 mm to metres.

1 mm is one thousandth of a metre or 0.001 m

23 mm is 0.023 m so 15 m 23 mm = 15.023 m

Answer: 15 m 23 mm = 15.023 m

> Note the zero between the 15 and the 23.

---

1 Convert the following measures.
  a 24.5 m into km _____
  b 0.05 g into mg _____
  c 15.4 m into mm _____
  d 5 cl into litres _____
  e 2 kg 5 g into kg _____
  f 10 cm 8.9 mm into metres _____

Imperial/metric units

- Learn the rough metric equivalents of Imperial units that are still in everyday use. For example:

> They are called Imperial as they date back to the British Empire.

An inch is 2.54 cm.
A foot (12 inches) is about 30 cm.
A yard (3 feet) is about 90 cm.
5 miles is about 8 kilometres.
A nautical mile is about 1.15 land miles.

An acre is about 0.4 hectares.
A pound is about 454 grams.
A stone (14 pounds) is about 6.4 kg.
A pint is about 0.6 litres.
A gallon (8 pints) is about 4.5 litres.

> A nautical mile (n.m.) makes an angle of 1 minute at the centre of the Earth. A knot is a speed of 1 n.m. per hour.

> Find out the history of some Imperial units.

Time with a calculator

- Time is not based on the decimal system! Do not change 3.5 hours (3 h 30 min) into 3 h 5 min, or 3 h 50 min.
- **Entering time into a calculator**

Example:
To enter 3 hours 25 minutes:

| 3 | + | 2 | 5 | ÷ | 6 | 0 | = |

• Converting a calculator decimal time

Example:

8.35

If the calculator answer is 8.35 minutes,

the .35 is $0.35\,\text{min} = 0.35 \times 60\,\text{s} = 21\,\text{s}$.
8.35 minutes is 8 min 21 s.

8.35 minutes must not be read as 8 minutes 35 seconds.

You can use the DMS ° ' " angle key. Investigate!

Speed

• At a constant speed of 70 mph you will go 70 miles in one hour.
• You may find Figure M1:1 helpful. It shows that:

> speed equals distance over time,
> distance equals speed times time,
> time equals distance over speed.

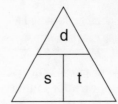

Figure M1:1

B

1 On the train timetable in Figure M1:2 the bolder, heavier times apply if you travel on the same train; the lighter times apply after changing to other trains. FO means Friday only, FX means Friday excepted (i.e. not Friday).

  a What time is the first train for Westbury from Paddington on a Monday after 1 p.m.? _____

  b How long does the 1646 from Westbury take to reach Newton Abbot? _____

  c Jim catches the 1207 from Taunton to Plymouth. If the trains are keeping to time, what is the earliest he could be in Plymouth? _____

  d It is 170 miles from Paddington to Exeter. What is the average speed of the fastest train shown? _____

2 This calculator sequence goes wrong. Why?
8 hours 25 minutes—4 hours 37 minutes.

| 8 | + | 2 | 5 | ÷ | 6 | 0 | − | 4 | + | 3 | 7 | ÷ | 6 | 0 | = |

3 Write down the keys you would press to find the answer to 23 minutes 45 seconds − 17 minutes 57 seconds.

4 A sprinter in lane 8 is 8 metres from the starting pistol. Sound travels at 340 metres per second. How much later does she hear it than the sprinter in lane 1, only 1 metre from it? The race is timed to the nearest hundredth of a second. Is this fair?

	BHX				✈ℝ	
London Paddington	**0745**	0815b	**0935**	**0945**	**1035**	**1135**
Heathrow Airport 🚇‡	0700	—	0845	—	0945	1045
Gatwick Airport	0559	—	0810	—	0920	1026
Reading	**0810**	0840b	**1002**	**1014**	**1102**	**1202**
Westbury	—	—	**1054**	—	—	**1246**
Castle Cary	—	—	—	—▸	—	**1303**
Taunton	**0951**	**1048**	**1131**	**1207**	—	**1326**
Tiverton Parkway	**1003**	—	**1143**	—	—	**1338**
Exeter St. Davids	**1018**	**1112**	**1158**	**1231**	**1237**	**1353**
Newton Abbot	**1041**	**1136**	**1222**	**1309**	1309	**1417**
Torquay	1112	1201	1253	1341	1341	1440
Paignton	1117	1208	1259	1446	1446	1446
Totnes	**1055**	**1148**	—	**1321**	1321	**1430**
Plymouth	**1126**	**1225**	**1303**	**1353**	**1338**	**1502**

	ℝFX	FO	FO	✈C	ℝ
London Paddington	**1235**	**1235**	**1335**	**1435**	**1535**
Heathrow Airport 🚇‡	1145	1145	1245	1345	1445
Gatwick Airport	1126	1126	1226	1326	1426
Reading	**1302**	**1302**	**1406**	**1502**	**1602**
Westbury	—	—	**1456**	—	**1646**
Castle Cary	—	—	—	—	—
Taunton	**1418**	**1418**	**1536**	**1618**	**1723**
Tiverton Parkway	—	—	—	**1630**	**1735**
Exeter St. Davids	**1442**	**1445**	**1603**	**1645**	**1750**
Newton Abbot	**1516**	**1516**	**1636**	**1709**	**1814**
Torquay	1544	1544	1649	1806	1837
Paignton	1549	1549	1655	1812	1842
Totnes	1528	1528	—	**1722**	**1827**
Plymouth	**1543**	1602	**1718**	**1753**	**1858**

Figure M1:2

M2 ● READING SCALES AND INSTRUMENTS

Clocks

- Analogue clocks have hands (Figure M2:1).
  Digital clocks just have figures.

DON'T	draw the hour hand at 2:30 like Figure M2:2 instead of like Figure M2:3.
DO	remember the hour hand does not suddenly jump an hour when the long hand reaches 12.

- The **12-hour clock** time uses a.m. (*ante* meaning before midday) and p.m. (*post* meaning after midday).
- The **24-hour clock** shows 1 p.m. as 1300. Add or subtract 12 when converting between 12-hour and 24-hour times.

DON'T	add or subtract 10 instead of 12, e.g. thinking that 1500 is 5 p.m.
DO	remember it is a *12-hour clock*.

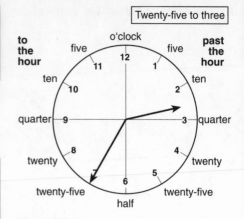

Twenty-five to three

Figure M2:1

Wrong!   Right!

Figure M2:2   **Figure M2:3**

A

1 Write the times on the clocks in Figure M2:4.
  (i) as figures in 12-hour clock time
  (ii) in words using 'past' or 'to'
  (iii) in 24-hour-clock time if it is a.m.
  (iv) in 24-hour-clock time if it is p.m.

a (i) _____ (ii) _____
  (iii) _____ (iv) _____
b (i) _____ (ii) _____
  (iii) _____ (iv) _____
c (i) _____ (ii) _____
  (iii) _____ (iv) _____
d (i) _____ (ii) _____
  (iii) _____ (iv) _____
e (i) _____ (ii) _____
  (iii) _____ (iv) _____

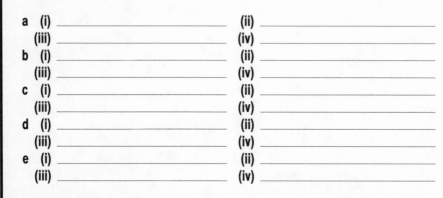

Figure M2:4

2 Draw hands on the clocks in Figure M2:5 to show the following times.

a twenty-five minutes past eleven   **b** twenty to two   **c** five to five   **d** 1645   **e** 0020

Figure M2:5

Reading scales and dials

DON'T	assume all scales always have ten divisions.
DO	count the divisions between the whole numbers printed on the scale and work out what each division represents.

B

1 What are the readings at the arrows on these scales?

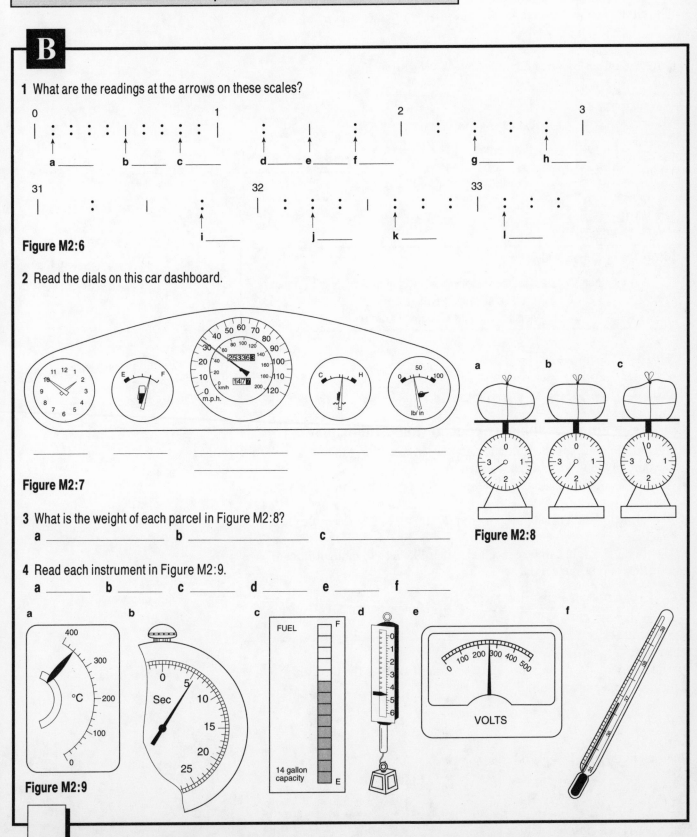

Figure M2:6

2 Read the dials on this car dashboard.

Figure M2:7

3 What is the weight of each parcel in Figure M2:8?

a _____ b _____ c _____

Figure M2:8

4 Read each instrument in Figure M2:9.

a _____ b _____ c _____ d _____ e _____ f _____

Figure M2:9

M3 ● MEASURING SHAPES

The Greek letter π (pi) stands for the result of dividing the circumference by the diameter, and is equal to about 3.14.

Perimeter
- The **perimeter** is the distance round the outside edges of a shape.
- The **circumference** of a circle is π times the diameter, or $C = \pi d$.

The perimeter of a circle is called its circumference.

Area
Try to remember the area formulae given in Figure M3:1.

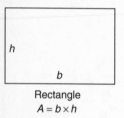

Rectangle
$A = b \times h$

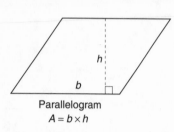

Parallelogram
$A = b \times h$

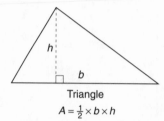

Triangle
$A = \frac{1}{2} \times b \times h$

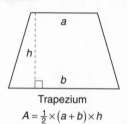

Trapezium
$A = \frac{1}{2} \times (a+b) \times h$

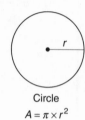

Circle
$A = \pi \times r^2$

Figure M3:1

DON'T mix up $C = \pi d$ and $A = \pi r^2$.

DO remember $C = \pi d$ must be a length formula as number × length = length
$A = \pi r^2$ must be an area formula as
number × length × length = area

A triangle has three heights, as any side can be the base.

Volume
- Volume of a prism = cross-section area × length
- Volume of a pyramid = $\frac{1}{3}$ base-area × height

The cross-section of a prism is the shape of the face when the prism is cut perpendicularly across its length.

Distinguishing formulae by considering dimensions
- A length formula may contain lengths **added** together, but will not contain any lengths **multiplied** together.
- An area formula must have, or simplify to, two lengths multiplied together.
- A volume formula must have, or simplify to, three lengths multiplied together.
- Units in a formula can be cancelled rather like letters in algebraic fractions can be cancelled.

$$\frac{\text{cm} \times \text{cm} \times \text{cm}}{\text{cm}} = \frac{\cancel{\text{cm}} \times \text{cm} \times \text{cm}}{\cancel{\text{cm}}} = \text{cm}^2 \text{ which is an area.}$$

Example:
In the following formula a, b, c and d are lengths. Does the formula give a length, an area, or a volume?

$$F = \frac{4a(b+c)}{\pi d}$$

$4a$ is a length, so is $(b+c)$ and so is πd.

$$\text{Hence } \frac{\text{cm} \times \text{cm}}{\text{cm}} = \frac{\cancel{\text{cm}} \times \text{cm}}{\cancel{\text{cm}}} = \text{cm}$$

Answer: It is a length formula.

A

1 Find the area of the garden shown in Figure M3:2.

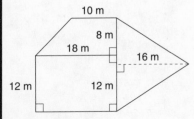

Figure M3:2

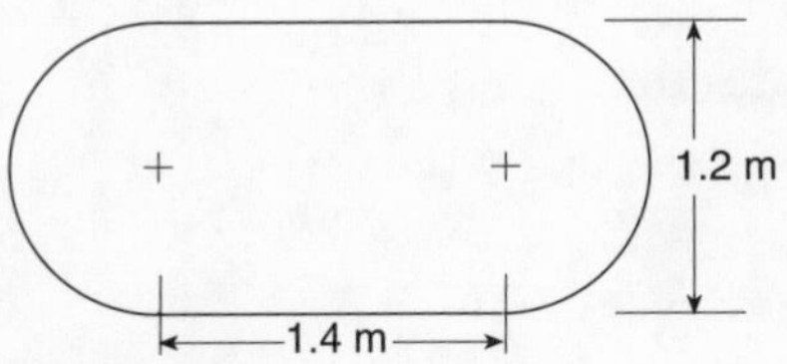

Figure M3:3

2 Figure M3:3 shows the cross-section of a drainage pipe. The sides are semicircles. Calculate, correct to three significant figures:

a the perimeter of the cross-section _____

b the area of the cross-section _____

c the area of metal needed to make a 10-metre pipe _____

d the capacity of a 10 metre length of pipe. _____

> Capacity is the volume of liquid a container can hold.

3 Calculate the weight of the post shown in Figure M3:4, if 1 cm³ of wood weighs 0.7 grams.

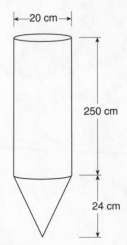

Figure M3:4

4 Describe these formulae as length, area, volume or impossible where b, h, l, d, r, x and y are all lengths.

a $F = \frac{1}{2}\pi h(1+x)$ _____

b $F = \frac{1}{2}bh^2$ _____

c $F = 2\pi r^2(x+y)$ _____

d $F = \dfrac{5hl(x+y)}{b}$ _____

e $F = 2\pi r^2hd$ _____

f $F = \dfrac{4(d+r)(x-y)}{b}$ _____

g $F = d(\frac{1}{2}bh+l)$ _____

5 Jen cannot remember whether the area of a circle is πr^2 or $2\pi r$. Explain how she can easily pick the correct one.

_____

_____

M4 ● PYTHAGORAS' THEOREM

Pythagoras' theorem

Pythagoras' theorem is used to calculate the third side of a right-angled triangle when the other two are known.

- In Figure M4:1 Pythagoras' theorem states that

$$h^2 = a^2 + b^2.$$

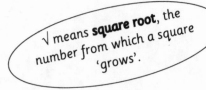

h stands for **hypotenuse**, the side under, or opposite, the right angle.

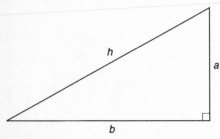

Figure M4:1

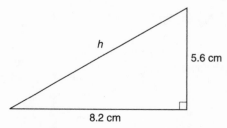

Figure M4:2

Example:

Calculate h in Figure M4:2.

$$h^2 = 5.6^2 + 8.2^2$$

$$= 31.36 + 67.24 = 98.60$$

Answer: $h = \sqrt{98.60} \approx 9.93 \, \text{cm}$

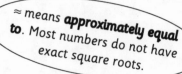

$\sqrt{\ }$ means **square root**, the number from which a square 'grows'.

- When finding one of the shorter sides, **subtract** the squares, that is $a^2 = h^2 - b^2$.

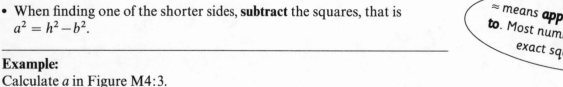

$\approx$ means **approximately equal to**. Most numbers do not have exact square roots.

Example:

Calculate a in Figure M4:3.

$$a^2 = 9.5^2 - 5.7^2$$

$$= 90.25 - 32.49 = 57.76$$

Answer: $a = \sqrt{57.76} = 7.6 \, \text{cm}$

- **Sample calculator key sequence**

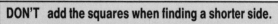

| 9 | . | 5 | x^2 | − | 5 | . | 7 | x^2 | = | $\sqrt{\ }$ |

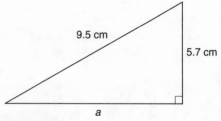

Figure M4:3

DON'T	add the squares when finding a shorter side.
DO	think whether you are finding the longest side or a shorter one before you start your answer.

1 Calculate, correct to three significant figures, the lengths of the unknown sides in Figure M4:4.

a   **b**   **c**   **d**

h _____   *p* _____   *g* _____   *n* _____

a   **b**   **c**   **d**

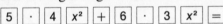

Figure M4:4

Applications of Pythagoras' theorem

Example:

In Figure M4:5, is angle C a right angle? Show your working.

If C is a right angle then $5.4^2 + 6.3^2$ must equal 8^2 which is 64.

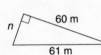

This does not come to 64 so angle C is not a right angle.

Note: If you were asked if angle CDB or CBD was a right angle, you could say, 'No, because a right angle must be the largest angle in a triangle, and that is always opposite the longest side.'

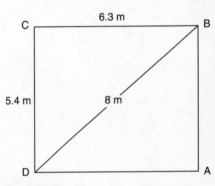

Figure M4:5

Example:

Can a 10 cm handle fit into the rectangular box shown in Figure M4:6?

The longest possible length for the handle is the diagonal from P to T.

The diagonal PR can be found from

$$PR^2 = PQ^2 + QR^2$$
$$= 5^2 + 6^2$$

The diagonal PT can be found from

$$PT^2 = PR^2 + RT^2$$
$$= 5^2 + 6^2 + 7^2$$

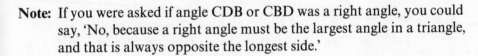

Answer: As PT $\approx$ 10.48 cm the 10 cm handle will fit at an angle across the box.

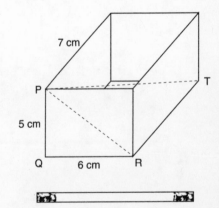

Figure M4:6

B

1 The garden in Figure M4:7 is to be fenced around its perimeter except for the 12 m side. The triangle is isosceles. Calculate the length of the fence.

_____ m

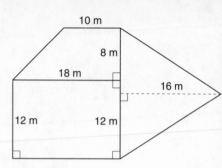

Figure M4:7

2 Figure M4:8 shows a moulding. Calculate:

a the area of the pentagonal face

_____ cm²

b the volume of the moulding

_____ cm³

c the total length of all the edges.

_____ cm

Figure M4:8

3 Figure M4:9 shows the cross-section of a girder.

a Calculate the perimeter and area of the cross-section.

_____ cm

_____ cm²

b The length of the girder is 500 cm. Calculate its volume in m³.

_____ m³

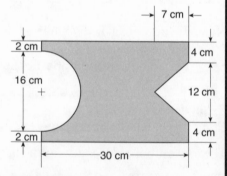

Figure M4:9

M5 ● TRIGONOMETRY

Tangent

- Figure M5:1 shows the sides of a right-angled triangle named to show their position relative to one of the non-right angles, here marked θ.
- For any one value of θ the result of dividing the length of the opposite side by the length of the adjacent side is always the same for any size triangle. It is called the **tangent** of the angle.

This is usually remembered as $\dfrac{o}{a} = \tan$.

It follows that $o = a \times \tan$.

- The value of the tangent for any angle is programmed into your calculator. It can be found using the $\boxed{\text{TAN}}$ key.

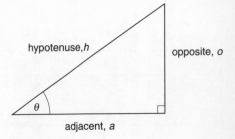

Figure M5:1

Example:
In Figure M5:2

AB is opposite to the 35° angle

BC is adjacent to the 35° angle.

So $o = a \times \tan \rightarrow \text{AB} = 6.4\,\text{cm} \times \tan 35°$

$\boxed{6}\ \boxed{.}\ \boxed{4}\ \boxed{\times}\ \boxed{3}\ \boxed{5}\ \boxed{\text{TAN}}\ \boxed{=}$

Answer: 4.48 cm

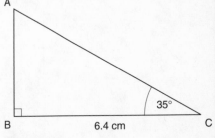

Figure M5:2

- At the time of writing most calculators' $\boxed{\text{TAN}}$ keys operate immediately on what is in the display, so you need to key in the 35 before pressing $\boxed{\text{TAN}}$.
- Calculators allow for angles to be measured in degrees, radians, or gradians, set by a $\boxed{\text{DRG}}$ key or a Mode. At this stage you should use degrees.

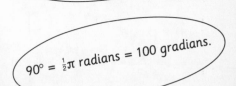

> **DO** Make sure your calculator is set to degrees. This shows in the window as D or DEG. The $\boxed{\text{DRG}}$ or a Mode Key is used to change between the three kinds of measure.
>
> **DON'T** Press $\boxed{\text{TAN}}$ before you have keyed in the angle unless your calculator allows this.

- Sometimes the side you are trying to find is opposite the blank angle. Use the angle sum of a triangle to calculate the size of this angle, then proceed as usual.
- The tangent rule can also be used to calculate the size of the non-right angles. The inverse $\boxed{\text{TAN}}$ is used to find the angle. This is usually marked $\boxed{\text{TAN}^{-1}}$ or $\boxed{\text{ARCTAN}}$ and probably needs the $\boxed{\text{SHIFT}}$ / $\boxed{\text{INV}}$ / $\boxed{\text{2nd F}}$ key as well.

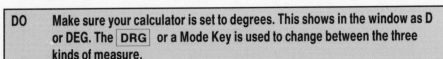

Example:
In Figure M5:3

$$\frac{o}{a} = \tan \rightarrow \frac{3.8}{4.6} = \tan \theta$$

| 3 | · | 8 | ÷ | 4 | · | 6 | = | INV | TAN |

Answer: $\theta = 39.6°$

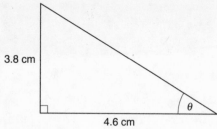

Figure M5:3

DON'T Press = after INV TAN .

DO Check your answer is reasonable (as always!).

A

1 Calculate the sides *x* and angles θ in Figure M5:4.

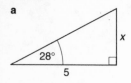 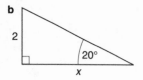 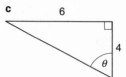 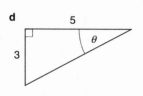 

Figure M5:4

2 Make up some more questions for yourself and check your answers by scale drawing.

Sine and cosine

- **Sines** and **cosines** (sin and cos) work in the same way as tangents, but use the hypotenuse and one other side.

Example:
In Figure M5:5

$$\text{opposite} = \text{hypotenuse} \times \sin \theta$$

$$\text{adjacent} = \text{hypotenuse} \times \cos \theta$$

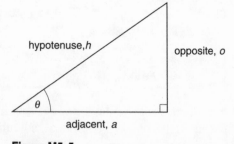

Figure M5:5

- The full set of rules can be remembered by:
  One **A**ncient **T**eacher **O**f **H**istory **S**wore **A**t **H**is **C**lass, or *oat ohs ahc.*

$$oat \rightarrow o = a \times \tan \text{ and } \frac{o}{a} = \tan$$

$$ohs \rightarrow o = h \times \sin \text{ and } \frac{o}{h} = \sin$$

$$ahc \rightarrow a = h \times \cos \text{ and } \frac{a}{h} = \cos$$

- The cosine is not strictly necessary, as the opposite and adjacent sides can be switched by using the other angle.

Example:
In Figure M5:6

$p = 10 \times \sin 30°$ or $p = 10 \times \cos 60°$

$q = 10 \times \cos 30°$ or $q = 10 \times \sin 60°$

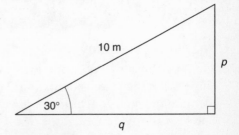

Figure M5:6

- The hypotenuse may be found either by using Pythagoras' theorem (Section M4) once the other two sides are known, or by changing the subject of the sine or cosine formulae to give:

$$h = \frac{o}{\sin} \quad \text{and} \quad h = \frac{a}{\cos}$$

DO only use the above rules in right-angled triangles.

B

1 Find x and θ in Figure M5:7.

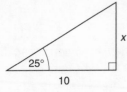

a _____

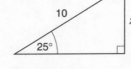

b _____

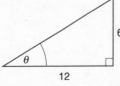

c _____

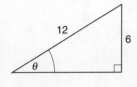

d _____

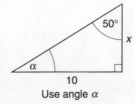

Use angle α

e _____

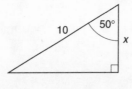

f _____

Figure M5:7

2 An aeroplane flies 50 km on a bearing of 040°, then turns to a bearing of 300° for 75 km.
a Calculate how far it is north and west of its starting point.

_____

b Calculate the bearing and direct distance of the aeroplane from its starting point.

_____

D1 ● COLLECTING INFORMATION

Conducting a survey

- A survey collects facts or opinions, usually by **sampling**, which is asking only part of the whole population. The larger the sample, the more accurate the final conclusions will be.
- The data should represent the whole population. Ways of doing this include **random** and **stratified** sampling.
- Random sampling aims to give every individual an equal chance of being surveyed, possibly by numbering everyone, then selecting with a **random number generator**.
- Stratified sampling tries to ensure all sections, or strata, are fairly represented. For example, in sampling a school the final report could represent equally the views of pupils in each year by asking the same number of pupils from each year, selecting these within each year-stratum by a random method.

Observation sheets

These are used to collect data. To avoid mistakes they need to be easy to use and clear. Headed columns are useful. It is wise to do a **dummy run**, so that improvements can be made. The **tally** method helps record large quantities of data quickly; see section D2.

Originally tallies were notches cut on a **tally stick**.

Questionnaires

- Questions must be designed to gather honest information.
  Questions must not be:
  - embarrassing
  - overheard or read by people who know the interviewee
  - ambiguous or difficult to understand
  - slanted to encourage a certain answer
  - critical of people's lifestyle or views.

When you **must** ask embarrassing questions it is best to use an anonymous written questionnaire.

Ambiguous means having more than one meaning.

- It will be very difficult to process data if you give people the freedom to say or write anything in their answers.
  Instead use:
  - questions to which the answer is yes/no/don't know
  - a choice of answers (**multi-choice**) where people pick one (It is sensible to include the choice 'None of these'.)
  - a statement with which people can: strongly agree/agree/no comment/disagree/strongly disagree.

Specifying a hypothesis

Surveys are often undertaken to see if there is any truth in a statement. Such a statement is called a **hypothesis**.

Example:
'Pupils get a better education in single-sex schools' is a hypothesis.

How would you define a 'better education'?

A

1 A large company with centres in five different areas of the UK wants to find out the likely reaction of its workforce to a new policy on pay and conditions.
Martha has to sample the views of 500 of its workforce. How should she select which workers to ask?

_____
_____
_____
_____
_____
_____

2 Criticise the following questions asked by a council trying to find out how people will react to plans to change the area they control.

a What are your views on the new council area plans?

_____
_____

b Do you really want Whitehall to change your council area?

_____
_____

c What do you think are the benefits of changing your council's area?

_____
_____

d 'Small is beautiful.' Don't you agree?

_____
_____

e It is proposed to split Stourset into three smaller council areas. Do you agree with this plan/disagree with it/not mind what happens?

_____
_____

f Your present council has let your area become a slum. Wouldn't you prefer more local management?

_____
_____

g 'Good evening. Your council wants to know your views on the proposed council areas. Firstly, what is your name? Are you male or female? Have you a live-in partner? If so, are you married or just living together? Finally, what changes would you like to see in your council areas?'

_____
_____

3 Think of a hypothesis about pupils in your school, then carry out a survey to see if it is true.

D2 ● PROCESSING INFORMATION

Tallyings

- To **tally** is to read raw data, recording each item in a table. Usually every fifth mark connects the previous four, so 7 items would be shown as ⫼⫼ //.

> Raw data is as collected, before any work has been done on it.

| DO | go through the list once only, tallying each item as you come to it. |

Frequency table for discrete data

- **Discrete** data falls into separate sections. No item of data comes between the sections. For example, numbers of pets are discrete data.
  Tallies are often used when drawing up a frequency table.

> Frequency means how many.

Example:

Number of sisters	Tally	Frequency
0	////	4
1	⫼⫼ //	7
2	///	3
	Total	14

Frequency table for continuous data

- **Continuous data** does not fall exactly into separate sections. For example, heights and masses are continuous data.

Example:
Discrete: Shirt collar sizes (14 $14\frac{1}{2}$ 15 etc.)

Continuous: Neck measurements

> What collar size would you buy for a $14\frac{1}{4}$ inch neck measurement?

- The data is grouped into **classes**.

Example:

Miles	0–9	10–19	20–29	30–39

- You have to decide whether data between the classes should count in the class below or the class above.

Example:
Distance walked, to the nearest mile

$9\frac{1}{2}$ miles counts as 10 miles.

$11\frac{1}{4}$ counts as 11 miles but $11\frac{3}{4}$ counts as 12 miles.

> Half-way is usually rounded up.

Example:
Qualifying age in years

15 years 1 day counts as 15 years.

15 years 11 months 27 days counts as 15 years.

16 years 1 day counts as 16 years.

Part years are ignored.

Example:
Cost of sending a parcel, weighed to the nearest 10 g

2.010 kg costs the same as a 3.000 kg parcel.

2.990 kg costs the same as a 3.000 kg parcel.

3.010 kg costs the same as a 4.000 kg parcel.

All weights are rounded up to next kg.

A

1 The following marks were obtained in a test. Using a tally to help you, draw up a grouped frequency table, using classes 0–9, 10–19 etc.

3, 12, 25, 15, 38, 13, 23, 18, 25, 8, 21, 14, 33, 24,
34, 16, 17, 26, 17, 21, 27, 30, 39, 19, 41, 20, 18, 21,
39, 12, 33, 30, 5, 25, 9, 21, 11, 35, 36, 12, 28, 6, 7,
35, 26, 40, 13, 24, 33, 21, 35, 15, 23, 27, 16, 23, 21,
45, 18, 23, 24, 33, 27, 7, 32, 8, 21, 24, 9, 25, 21, 6,
29, 17, 29, 29, 18, 25, 12, 49, 29, 30, 39, 16, 23, 34,
15, 32, 19, 31, 23, 42, 21, 40, 22, 41, 43, 27, 45, 28.

0–9		
10–19		
20–29		
30–39		
40–49		

2 In each of the following, say into which of the two given classes you would place the given items of data. Give reasons for your choices.

a Length of tail (nearest mm): 15.8 cm, 15.3 cm.

Classes (cm):   10–15   16–20

_____

_____

_____

b Capacity of compartment (passengers): 140, 135, 142

Classes (passengers):   131–140   141–150

_____

_____

_____

c Age at marriage (years/months): 17y 3m, 21y 10m, 25y 2m

Classes (years):   Under 17   17 to 21   22 to 25   over 25

_____

_____

_____

D3 ● REPRESENTING INFORMATION

Pictogram

A picture or symbol represents each item, or a number of items, of the data; see Figure D3:1. Pictograms are attractive but cannot accurately show fractions of the data.

Figure D3:1

Bar chart

Bar charts represent discrete data, using columns or horizontal bars. The length of each bar represents the frequency of the data. The bars can have spaces between them or they can touch, see Figure D3:2.

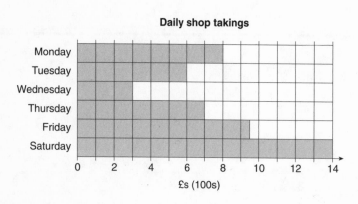

Daily shop takings

£s (100s)

Figure D3:2

See Section D2 for the difference between discrete and continuous data.

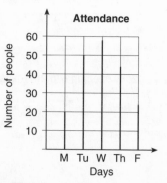

Favourite season

Joy			
Fay			
Alan	Joe		
Roy	Sam	Tom	Ann
Jim	Sue	Bob	Raj

Summer   Autumn
   Spring   Winter

Figure D3:3

Block graph

The block graph is like a bar chart except that the bars are made up of separate blocks, see Figure D3:3. As each block represents a certain amount, there is no need for a vertical scale, so it should not really be called a graph!

Bar line chart

These are also known as **vertical line diagrams**, **stick graphs** or **frequency bar diagrams**.
Instead of wide bars, single lines are drawn, see Figure D3:4.

Composite bar chart

This is sometimes called a **proportionate bar chart**. The total frequency is represented by one bar, divided up into sections (often as percentages of the whole), see Figure D3:5.

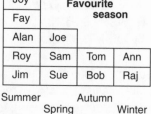

Attendance

Number of people

M Tu W Th F
Days

Figure D3:4

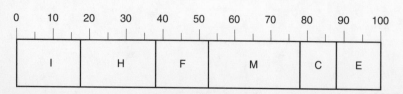

| I | H | F | M | C | E |

Figure D3:5

Pie chart

The total frequency is shared among the 360° that make a full turn, and each item is given a slice of the pie.

In Figure D3:6, 100% is 360°, so 1% is 3.6°.

The sector showing cakes is $6 \times 3.6° = 21.6°$.

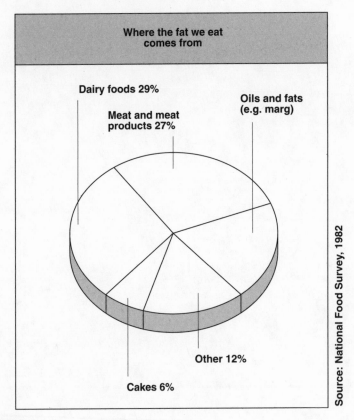

Where the fat we eat comes from

Dairy foods 29%

Meat and meat products 27%

Oils and fats (e.g. marg)

Other 12%

Cakes 6%

Source: National Food Survey, 1982

Figure D3:6

In a histogram it is the area of the bar that represents the frequency, not the height, unless all bars are equal width.

Grouped frequency diagram

These are bar charts for grouped frequency. Sometimes they are just called **frequency diagrams**, though all statistical charts represent frequency.

They are also sometimes called **histograms**, but this is not strictly correct.

- Discrete or continuous data may be grouped into classes, and the frequency for each class illustrated by a bar.

  If the data is discrete the bars need not touch each other.

  If the data is continuous they **must** touch, the dividing lines being drawn at the deciding value for inclusion in the next class up, see Figure D3:7.

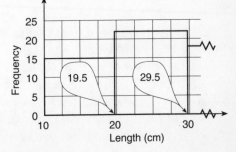

Figure D3:7

DON'T write 10–19, 20–29, etc. under the bars when the data is continuous.

DO use a normal scale marked 0, 10, 20 etc. starting each bar at the changeover value.

Frequency polygon line graph

In a **frequency polygon** the frequency is plotted over the value of the data and the points are joined with a line.

A dotted line should be used for non-continuous data, to indicate that points between the plotted ones have no meaning.

If the data is grouped, the points are plotted above the middle of each class interval, see Figure D3:8.

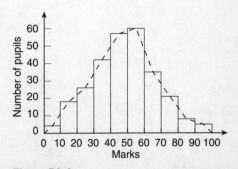

Figure D3:8

A

1 Illustrate the following data with a pictogram, a block graph, a bar chart, a bar line chart, a composite bar chart and a pie chart.

Average number of days of holiday for workers

Japan	USA	UK	France	Germany
9	19	24	26	29

2 Draw a grouped frequency diagram, then join the midpoints of the tops of the bars to make a grouped frequency polygon for the following data. Each bar should be 2 cm wide.

a

Weight (kg)	0–4	5–9	10–14	15–19
Frequency	5	12	8	3

Note: Weights are to the nearest kilogram.

b

Age (years)	0–4	5–9	10–14	15–19
Frequency	5	12	8	3

Note: Part years are ignored.

Scatter graph

• Scatter graphs are not used to illustrate data, but to search for any connection between two sets of data.

Figure D3:9 shows positive **correlation** between weight and height. Generally, taller people weigh more than shorter people.

Figure D3:10 shows negative (or **inverse**) correlation between the age of adults and the time they can run without resting. Generally, the older the person, the shorter time they can keep running.

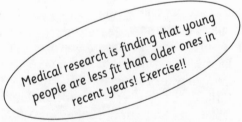
Medical research is finding that young people are less fit than older ones in recent years! Exercise!!

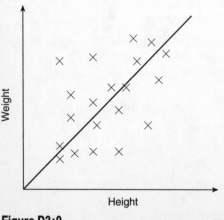
Figure D3:9

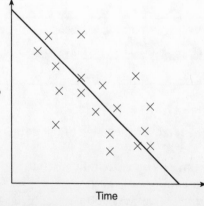
Figure D3:10

Figure D3:11 shows that your weight has no correlation with your artistic ability.
- A **line of best fit** can be drawn when there is correlation. It should be drawn through the data so that the same number of points are above it as below it. It should also pass through the point representing the means of the two sets of data, but KS3 tests may not expect this.

> **DON'T** think the line of best fit has to pass through as many points as possible.
>
> **DON'T** think the line of best fit has to join the two end points.
>
> **DON'T** draw a wide band, just draw one line.

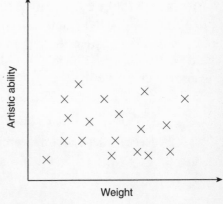

Figure D3:11

B

1 Sketch a possible scatter of points for a scatter graph that has for its axes each of the following pairs.
- **a** height of a person/arm length
- **b** number of holes per m² in fishnet/fish population where net used
- **c** number of km of hedges in UK/number of wild animals in UK
- **d** age of a car/number of passengers in it.

2

Age	5	5	5	6	6	6	7	7	7	8	8	8	9	9	9	10	10	10
Amount (p)	25	75	200	50	80	125	25	80	250	100	200	350	125	200	275	75	175	250
% saved	25	60	40	50	35	80	75	5	10	5	50	0	25	45	50	80	90	10
Bros/Sists	5	4	3	5	2	2	1	0	2	3	2	1	3	0	1	4	1	3

11	11	11	12	12	12	13	13	13	14	14	14	15	15	15	16	16	16
225	230	275	200	250	225	100	200	200	200	275	300	250	275	350	100	325	350
15	35	80	0	75	30	20	50	55	90	0	10	20	20	70	0	60	10
1	2	1	0	1	3	2	1	2	0	4	2	2	1	2	4	1	0

The table shows facts about weekly pocket money. Use scatter graphs, including a line of best fit where possible, to identify correlation between:
- **a** age and pocket money
- **b** number of brothers/sisters and pocket money
- **c** amount received and percentage saved.

Cumulative frequency curve/polygon

This shows how the data builds up, or **accumulates**.
First you add the frequencies to draw up the **cumulative frequency table**.
These are then plotted and joined (either with a smooth curve, or as a
polygon) to give, usually, a roughly S-shaped line (Figure D3:12).

Example: See Figure D3:12.

Class	Frequency	Cumulative frequency
0–10	3	3
11–20	6	3+6 = 9
21–30	7	9+7 = 16
31–50	4	16+4 = 20

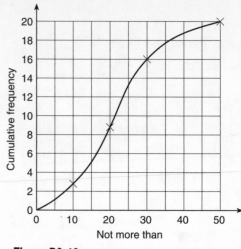

Figure D3:12

DO   always put frequencies on the VERTICAL axis.

DON'T use frequencies when told to use cumulative frequencies.

Quartiles are explained in Section D4.

 C

1 Complete the cumulative frequency row, then draw a cumulative frequency
polygon.

Height (cm)	0–9	10–19	20–29	30–39	40–49	50–59	60–100
Frequency	3	7	8	11	12	7	5

Height (not more than)	9.5	19.5	29.5	39.5	49.5	59.5	100
Cumulative frequency	3	10					

2 Make at least two observations about the differences between the men's and the
women's wages shown in Figure D3:13.

_____

_____

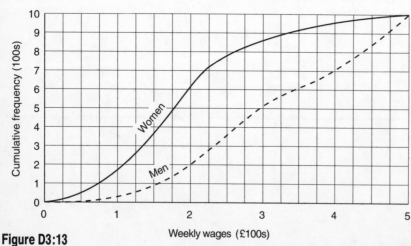

Figure D3:13

D4 ● INTERPRETING INFORMATION

Measuring dispersion

- A **normal distribution** of data has most items clustered towards the middle of the whole spread of values, gradually tailing off each side to give a bell-shaped curve.
- To investigate data we collect various averages and ranges to try to give a picture of how normal the distribution is.
- At this stage you need to know how to calculate the **median**, the **mean**, the **mode**, the **range** and the **interquartile range**. Taken together these can give a fair picture of the data, although one value on its own can be very misleading.

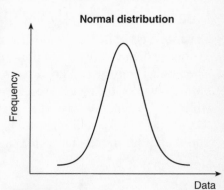

Figure D4:1

Median

- This is the value which has half the data above it and half below.
- In a normal distribution the median is half-way between the highest and the lowest possible values.
- For just a few items of data, the best way to find the median is to write the data in order of size, so you can see where the middle value is. For an even number of items of data the median is taken as half-way between the middle two items.

> An average is an attempt to represent a whole range of data by one measure, for example, the average age of brides.

Example:

Find the median of 3, 5, 6, 5, 7, 2, 8, 9, 7, 9.

Rewrite in order: 2, 3, 5, 5, 6, 7, 7, 8, 9, 9.

The median is 6.5, half-way between 6 and 7.

> To find half-way between two numbers, add them then divide by 2.

- For a large amount of data, sort it into classes first to find the class in which the middle value lies. You can then order just this class to find the exact median.

Example:

Number of sisters	Tally	Frequency
0	////	4
1	~~////~~ //	7
2	///	3
	Total	14

There are 14 items of data, the median is between item number 7 and 8.

Class 0 has 4 members. Class 1 has 7 members, making 11, so the 7th and 8th come into this class. Hence the median number of sisters is 1.

Example:

Height (m)	0–5	6–10	11–15	16–20	21–25	26–30
Frequency	25	46	67	37	42	19
Cumulative frequency	25	71	138	175	217	236

$236 \div 2 = 118$, so the median will be between the 118th and 119th items. From the cumulative frequency row we can see that it is in the class 11–15.

Given the full list of data, we could put in order just the values from 11 to 15 to find the median.

> 118.5 is more than 71 but less than 138.

Mode

- The mode is the item of data with the highest frequency. It is the only average which can represent non-numerical data, e.g. colours.
- The mode rarely gives a good picture of the distribution of numerical data. However, the **modal class**, or a value in that class, is valuable, and is what people generally use when they talk about an average. For example, 'On average I take an hour to do my homework,' probably means 'I take about an hour more often than any other time'.

The modal class is the one with the highest frequency.

Mean

- To find the mean we add all the data, then share it out equally.

DON'T	find the mean of COMPOUND units this way. The mean speed (usually just called average speed) of 20 mph and 100 mph is not $120 \div 2 = 60$ mph.
DO	remember that average speed equals total distance divided by total time.

Compound units are like miles per hour or grams per cm^3.

Example:

No. of pets	0	1	2	3	4	5	6
Frequency	4	5	7	6	3	2	1

The total number of pets is:

$(0 \times 4) + (1 \times 5) + (2 \times 7) + (3 \times 6) + (4 \times 3) + (5 \times 2) + (6 \times 1) = 65.$

The total frequency is $4 + 5 + 7 + 6 + 3 + 2 + 1 = 28.$
The mean is $65 \div 28 \approx 2.32$ pets per person.

DON'T	add up the number of pets $(0+1+2+3+4+5+6)$ and divide by 7.
DON'T	add the frequencies $(4+5+7+6+3+2+1)$.
DO	multiply number by frequency to find the totals.

- For grouped data every member of a class is taken to have scored the mid-value of that class. The 'too-big' and 'too-small' errors tend to cancel each other out.

To find the mid-value add up the two limits and divide by 2.

Example:

Height (m)	0–5	6–10	11–15	16–20	21–25	26–30	Total
Frequency	25	46	67	37	42	19	236

Total height is taken to be
$(2.5 \times 25) + (8 \times 46) + (13 \times 67) + (18 \times 37) + (23 \times 42) + (28 \times 19) = 3455.5$ m

The approximate mean is $3456 \div 236 \approx 14.6$ m.

DON'T	add the mid-points of classes or the given frequencies. That does not make any sense, but students are known to do it!

Range

- The range of the data is the difference between the highest and lowest item of data.

DON'T	give the range as £3 to £75.
DO	give the range as the difference, £72 is the range for £3 to £75.

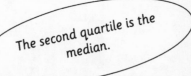

The second quartile is the median.

- The **quartiles** are the values of the data $\frac{1}{4}$, $\frac{1}{2}$ and $\frac{3}{4}$ of the way along it when in order.
- The interquartile range is the spread of the middle half of the data, that is the third quartile minus the first.

To find the values of the quartiles when you have drawn a cumulative frequency curve or polygon, divide the cumulative frequency axis into four equal parts, then go across to the curve and down to read the values on the other axis, see Figure D4:2.

Percentiles divide the range into 100 parts, so are more precise than quartiles.

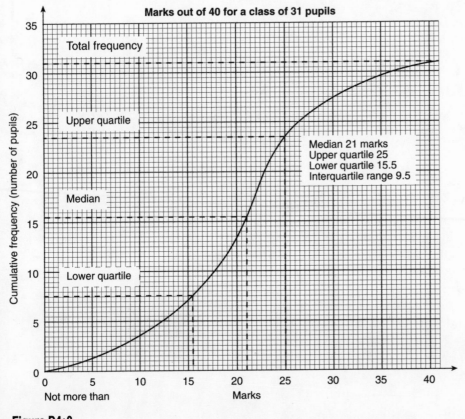

Figure D4:2

A

1 Find the mode, median, mean, range and interquartile range for each set of data.

a 3, 4, 3, 5, 6, 5, 7, 5, 4, 3, 5, 6, 7, 6, 8, 7, 9, 1, 2, 3, 2, 5, 4, 8, 6, 7, 6, 6, 5, 5, 4, 5, 4, 5, 6, 5

mode _____ median _____ mean _____

range _____ interquartile range _____

b

Volume (litres)	1	2	3	4	5	6
Frequency	3	5	6	5	4	1

mode _____ median _____ mean _____

range _____ interquartile range _____

c

Occupants	0	1	2	3	4	5	6	7	8
Frequency	9	3	5	3	1	6	4	8	8

mode _____ median _____ mean _____

range _____ interquartile range _____

2 Use the graph you drew for Section D3 Box C, question **1**, to estimate the value of the quartiles and the interquartile range of the heights.

quartiles _____

interquartile range _____

Comparing averages and dispersion

- For near normal data (see Figure D4:1, page 93) the mean, median and mode will all be approximately the same. If one is very different from the others it should not be used to represent the data. If all three are very different you know you have a non-normal set of data, but you cannot say much more (without using advanced statistics) unless you are given the actual data.

- When comparing the two sets of data, first make sure they are measuring the same thing. For example there is no sense in comparing the averages for number of pets with the averages for distance travelled per year. First compare the averages within each set, as explained above. Then compare the same averages for each set.

You could look for correlation between income and pets.

Example:

Marks out of 50 on the same test from two maths sets, A and B.

	Median	Mode	Mean	Range
Set A	31	27	29.4	20
Set B	32	5	39.4	50

Set A seems to have a normal shape distribution.

Set B has a strange mode, but this may not be significant. It should be ignored.

The classes have the same median, but Set B has a much wider range and a higher mean.

We might conclude that Set B has a wider spread of ability and more pupils who are good at maths than Set A.

To confirm the distribution is normal, we also need to know about standard deviation, which is not part of the work at this stage.

B

1 Comment on your answers to the questions in Box A on page 96. How well do you think your answers describe the data?

a _____

_____

b _____

_____

c _____

_____

2 A school reports that on average no pupil truants for more than one day a year. How might this conclusion be reached?

a _____

_____

b _____

_____

c _____

_____

3 Explain how:

a everyone can be average
b all but one of a class can have above average marks in a test only taken by that class.

a _____

_____

b _____

_____

4 A newspaper says the average UK income in 1993 was £190 a week. What do you think this means?

_____

_____

_____

5 Many people think the average must be in the middle. Why do you think this is?

_____

_____

D5 ● ONE-EVENT PROBABILITY

Measuring likelihood

- **Probability** predicts the likelihood or chance that a future event will happen. For example it might be impossible, unlikely, evens, highly probable, or certain.
- In mathematics we usually state chance as a fraction (common, decimal or percentage) on a probability scale of 0 to 1. Probability 0 means impossible, $\frac{1}{2}$ means evens and 1 means certain.

An event is something that happens.

Evens means just as likely to happen as not.

Collecting data

- When we know how often something should happen we can calculate its probability. We call this using **relative frequency**.
  For instance, a fair coin (one that has not been weighted) is equally likely to fall heads as tails, so we know that P(heads) = $\frac{1}{2}$. Out of 1000 throws we would expect about 500 heads and 500 tails.
  To check if a coin is fair we have to throw it many times to see if we do get about the same number of heads as tails. This is called **collecting data**.
- Some probabilities can **only** be found by collecting data.
  For instance, if we wanted to find out how likely a bus is to depart within five minutes of its planned time, we would have to check lots of buses over a long time. If we found that 100 buses out of 1000 were more than five minutes late leaving, then we could say P(bus leaving within five minutes of planned time) is 90%.

Odds are another way of stating probability. See the glossary.

P( ) means 'the probability of'

Estimating and experimenting

Probability does not tell us what **will** happen (unless P(outcome) = 1), only **how likely** it is to happen. We might base this on a calculation or on collected data.

We know that a fair die has a probability of $\frac{1}{6}$ that it will come up 6. This does not mean that if we throw it six times we will only get 6 once. It does mean that the number of sixes thrown ÷ the number of throws should get closer and closer to $\frac{1}{6}$ or 0.16̇. If it does not we would suspect that the die is not fair (or is **biased**), but even 6000 sixes in 6000 throws is not impossible, just extremely unlikely.

Trial is the testing out of an event.

Outcome is the result of a trial.

Die is the singular of dice: one die, two dice.

1 Use suitable words to describe the probability that:
  a the next dog you see has a tail _____
  b a person wearing glasses has perfect eyesight _____
  c a regular smoker is harming his or her health _____
  d a UK parliament lasts more than five years _____
  e you beat an equally able player at tennis _____
  f the next coin you are given is a 20p. _____

2 A packet of beads contains only red and green beads, but you do not know this.
  a You pick a bead at random, then replace it. What would you then know about the beads?
  _____
  _____

  b How would your knowledge of what is in the bag change when part **a** is repeated?
  _____
  _____
  _____

  c How could you calculate the probability of picking a red bead from the packet?
  _____
  _____

The probability rule

• If all the outcomes of an event are equally likely, then

$$P \text{ (successful outcome)} = \frac{\text{number of successful outcomes possible}}{\text{number of outcomes possible}}$$

> Many outcomes are not equally likely, e.g. a day can be wet or dry, but is P (rain tomorrow) = $\frac{1}{2}$?

Example:
Find P(picking a king from a pack of 52 cards).

The number of successful outcomes possible is four (there are four kings in the pack).

The number of possible outcomes is 52 (there are 52 cards in the pack).

So P(king) = $\frac{4}{52}$ or $\frac{1}{13}$.

Answer: P(king) = $\frac{1}{13}$

• P(an outcome happens) + P(that outcome does not happen) = 1.
  Remembering this can save a lot of calculation in later work.

Example:
The probability of a family of five having no boys in it is 0.031 25. What is the probability of a family of five having at least one boy?

As either there are 'no boys' or else there is 'at least one boy' these cover all possibilities, so their probabilities must total 1.

Answer: $1 - 0.03125 = 0.96875$

B

1 Pippa has bought ten raffle tickets and 1000 were sold. What is her chance of winning the first prize?

_____

2 A cricket match may end in a win or a draw. A coin is tossed to decide who bats first.
Explain why P(coin falls heads) is $\frac{1}{2}$ but P(result is a win) cannot be taken to be $\frac{1}{2}$.

_____

_____

3 Seven pupils out of 20 know the answer to a question. The teacher asks pupils at random for the answer.
a What is the highest number of pupils she could ask without getting the right answer?

_____

b What is P(the first pupil asked does not know the answer)?

_____

c Six pupils asked did not know the answer. What is P(the next pupil asked will know)?

_____

d Explain why P(the pupil asked gives the wrong answer) in part **c** may not be the same if he had been the first one asked, not the seventh.

_____

_____

_____

4 a Write out all possible orders of boys and girls in a family of four (e.g. BBGB). Set out your answer logically to reduce the chance of repeats or omissions.

_____

_____

_____

b What is the probability of a family of four having:

(i) all boys _____

(ii) equal boys and girls? _____

5 The probability of a certain battery giving 100 hours of useful life is 0.65. What is the probability it will fail before 100 hours are up?

_____

D6 ● COMBINED-EVENT PROBABILITY

Combining probabilities
- If only one of a set of outcomes can happen in one trial we say they are **mutually exclusive** (or just **exclusive**).
- If the outcome of one event does not affect the outcome of another, they are **independent**.
- A **tree diagram** is a useful way to represent all possible outcomes. One is shown in question **3** at the end of this section.

Exclusive means one happening shuts out (excludes) the rest.

Mutually exclusive outcomes
- When given a choice of successful outcomes add the probabilities of each, as the chance of success must increase.

Adding fractions makes a bigger fraction, i.e. more chance.

Example:
What is the probability of drawing a king or a queen from a pack of 52 cards?

We know P(king) $= \frac{1}{13}$ and P(queen) $= \frac{1}{13}$.

So P(king or queen) $= \frac{1}{13} + \frac{1}{13} = \frac{2}{13}$.

Answer: P(king or queen) $= \frac{2}{13}$

- You could also say that there are eight successful outcomes possible (any king + any queen). There are 52 cards that could be picked. Using the rule given in Section D5, P(king or queen) $= \frac{8}{52} = \frac{2}{13}$.

Independent events
- When events are combined the probability of one particular set of outcomes is found by multiplying their individual probabilities. These individual probabilities may be altered by previous events, when we say the events are 'dependent' or 'not independent'.

Multiplying fractions makes a smaller fraction, i.e. less chance.

Example:
Find P(throwing three heads in a row).

P(H) $= \frac{1}{2}$, so P(HHH) $= \frac{1}{2} \times \frac{1}{2} \times \frac{1}{2} = \frac{1}{8}$.

You could also list the outcomes.

HHH HHT HTH HTT THH THT TTH TTT

As only one of these eight has three heads, P(HHH) $= \frac{1}{8}$.

- P(outcome) $= 1 -$ P(not that outcome) should be used when possible.

Example:
Find P(at least one tail in five throws), when a fair coin is tossed.

First find P(no tails). No tails means all heads.

P(all heads) $= \frac{1}{2} \times \frac{1}{2} \times \frac{1}{2} \times \frac{1}{2} \times \frac{1}{2} = \frac{1}{32}$.

All other outcomes must have at least one tail.

Answer: P(at least one tail in five throws) is $1 - \frac{1}{32} = \frac{31}{32}$.

A

1 Tim sows part of a packet of seeds. He ends up with 25 red-flowered plants, 15 yellow and 10 white. He then sows the rest of the packet and selects two of the resulting plants before they flower.

Calculate the probability that their flowers will be:

a both red   _____

b neither red   _____

c neither white   _____

d one red and one yellow   _____

e one white and the other not white.   _____

2 A shop has a maximum length and weight of carrot for its 'Special Selection' pack. By sampling several boxes of carrots Ann calculates:
$P(\text{too long}) = 0.3$ and $(\text{too heavy}) = 0.4$.
a What is the probability that any carrot will be:

(i) too long and too heavy

        _____

(ii) OK for length but too heavy

        _____

(iii) OK for weight but too long

        _____

(iv) acceptable for the pack?

        _____

b How does the sum of your answers to part a help check you have not made a mistake?
_____
_____

c Fifty special 1 kg packs are to be made up. How many 25 kg boxes of carrots should be needed?

        _____

3 A driving test consists of a practical and a written paper. On the first time of testing P(passing the written paper) is $\frac{1}{2}$ and of passing the practical is $\frac{1}{4}$. Complete the tree diagram to show the four possible outcomes and their probabilities.

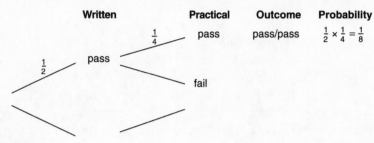

Written	Practical	Outcome	Probability

pass — $\frac{1}{2}$ · pass $\frac{1}{4}$ pass · pass/pass · $\frac{1}{2} \times \frac{1}{4} = \frac{1}{8}$

fail

Figure D6:1

4 Each contestant in a quiz is asked five questions. After 1000 questions it is found that 600 have been answered correctly. Bill says that means P(a contestant's answer is correct) is $\frac{600}{1000}$ or 0.6. Why is this faulty reasoning?

_____

_____

5 Year 9 in a school are divided into ten sets for Mathematics and English. Each set has the same number of pupils. A pupil is selected at random. Explain each of the following.

a P(the pupil is in set 1 for English) = 0.1 and P(the pupil is in set 1 for Mathematics) = 0.1.

_____

_____

b P(the pupil is in set 1 for both Mathematics and English) is not $0.1 \times 0.1 = 0.01$.

_____

_____

6 Nikki is waiting for a taxi. From past experience she thinks P(taxi will be black) is $\frac{7}{8}$ and P(driver will be female) is $\frac{1}{4}$. What is the probability that the taxi will either be black or will have a female driver?

_____

_____

_____

GLOSSARY

Using the glossary and the index

The **glossary** gives the meanings of words you might meet in questions, but which are not explained in the main part of this book.

The **index** gives you section references where topics and meanings may be found.

If you cannot find a multi-word expression, look for it under each word. For example, 'Area of trapezium' could be listed under 'Area' or under 'Trapezium'. Also try words like it, e.g. for 'symmetrical' look up the notes on 'symmetry'.

Altitude   Height measured from a chosen base line.

Apex   The top point, especially of a triangle and a cone.

Appreciation   The amount by which something has increased in value.

Ascending   Rising, e.g. 1, 3, 6, 10.

Billion   A thousand million. (A British billion used to be a million million, but is not used now.)

Binary   Arithmetic using only 0 and 1. Used by microchips.

Bisect   To cut into two equal parts.

Capacity   The amount of space inside a container.

Chain   Imperial measurement of 22 yards ($\approx$ 20 metres).

Circumcircle   The circle that, if possible, passes through all corners of a shape.

Complement   One of two parts that make up a whole. Complementary angles add up to 90°.

Concave   Curving or pointing inwards.

Concurrent   Meeting at the same point.

Conjecture   A guess or forecast without proof.

Consecutive   In *rank order* with no member of the set omitted, e.g. 3, 4, 5, 6 or 1, 4, 9, 16.

Constant   Not changing. The opposite of *variable*. E.g. 3 is a constant in 3*as*.

Converge   To move towards, or meet at, one point. See *diverge*.

Convert   To change, as in conversion graph.

Convex   Curving or pointing outwards.

Cubic   In the shape of a cube. Also an algebraic expression involving a term of third power, like $5x^3$.

Cyclic quadrilateral   One with its four corners on the circumference of a circle.

Decade   Ten years.

Deduce   To reach a conclusion by reasoning.

Deduction   Something taken away.

Density   The mass of an object, in grams per cm^3.

Depreciation   A drop in value.

Diagonal   A straight line joining two vertices of a polygon.

Difference   The result of subtracting a smaller number from a larger.

Direct proportion   Two amounts are in direct proportion when they change at the same rate.

Discount   The amount taken off a price.

Diverge   To move apart. See *converge*.

Empirical   Found by experiment or past experience.

Exchange rate   The amount of one country's currency that you can buy using another currency, e.g. £1 might buy $1.80.

Expression   A collection of terms with no equality, like $4x - 2y^2 + 3$.

Face   The flat side of a *polyhedron*.

Frustum (not Frustrum)   The part of a pyramid or cone between the base and a plane parallel to the base.

Googol 1×10^{100}, or 1 followed by 100 zeros!

Gross   Without any *deduction*. Also 144 items.

Hatch   To shade an area by drawing parallel sloping lines.

Horizontal   Across the page, as in horizon.

Incircle   A circle which, if possible, touches all the sides of a polygon.

Inclusive   Including both ends.

Increment   An increase.

Infinite   Without end.

Inflation   In finance, the decrease in the value of money, e.g. a loaf costing 12p in 1970 cost 70p in 1990.

Instalment   One of a series of payments.

Integer   A whole number, like 4 and −4. Zero is usually taken to be an even integer.

Intercept   Part of a line between two crossing points.

Interest   An amount paid by a borrower of money to the lender.

Intersection   The crossing point.

Invoice   A bill, setting out the payment required.

Irregular shape   One whose sides and angles are not all equal.

Iteration   Repetition.

Magnitude   Size.

Natural numbers   Numbers used for counting.
Network   A system of intersecting lines.
Node   A junction in a *network*.

Odds   Odds of 5 to 1 against means one chance that the outcome will be favourable, five chances that it will not, equivalent to probability $\frac{1}{6}$.
Ogive   Another name for the cumulative frequency curve.
Operation   In arithmetic, one of $+$, $-$, $\times$ and $\div$, or something else defined in a particular case.

Perpendicular   At right angles to another line or to a plane.
Polyhedron   Any solid made up of plane (flat) surfaces.
Produce   To make a line longer.

Quadrant   A quarter of a circle.

Rank order   In order, usually from smallest to biggest.
Real number   A number that exists, unlike $\sqrt{-1}$ which is unreal or imaginary.
Reciprocal   The reciprocal of x is $\frac{1}{x}$.
Rectangular number   Any number which is not prime (though 1 is doubtful).
Redundancy   Losing your job because there is no work for you to do.

Salary   The amount a worker is to receive for a year's work, usually paid monthly.
Score   Twenty. Also the total made.
Secant   A straight line cutting a circle.
Sector   Part of a circle bounded by two radii and an arc.
Segment   Part of a circle bounded by a chord and an arc.
Subtend   Angle APB is subtended at a point P by the lines AP and BP.
Symbol   A letter or a sign to represent something else. In mathematics and science a letter usually represents a number, but sometimes it represents a measurement, like h for height.

Tangent   A straight line which touches a curve, but never crosses it. Also a term in trigonometry.
Tariff   A table of prices.
Tessellation   A pattern of shapes which entirely covers a surface.
Trundle wheel   A wheel of standard circumference, usually a metre, rolled along the ground to measure distance.

Unbiased   Free from prejudice.

Variable   Liable to change, like the letters in algebra.
VAT   Value added tax. A tax put on goods and services by the Government.
Vertical   Upright, or going towards the top of a page.

INDEX

ANSWERS

Number

N1
Box A
1 a eight thousand, one hundred and five
  b fifty thousand and three
  c three hundred million, five hundred thousand

2 a 2020   **b** 56 500 000

3 9, 55, 66, 89, 306, 890, 984, 1001

N2
Box A
1 a sixteen point zero three five
  b one thousand point zero zero one

2 a 7 tens   **b** 7 hundredths   **c** 7 thousandths

3 3.901, 3.9, 3.55, 3.5, 3.25, 3.08, 3.059, 3

4 1.5 is displayed instead of 1.50, unless the calculator's floating point is fixed to two decimal places. The final zero is not strictly necessary but is used to avoid reading £1.5 as £1 and 5 pence.

5 a 8500   **b** 6500   **c** 52

6 a 9.7   **b** 0.46   **c** 0.01582

7 1 000 000

8 The figures (or the point if you prefer) are moved left or right by the same number of places (columns) as there are noughts.

N3
Box A

1 a
$$\begin{array}{r} 3\;6\;.\;7 \\ +\quad 8 \\ \hline 4\;4\;.\;7 \\ \hline {\scriptstyle 1} \end{array}$$

b (Note the zero)
$$\begin{array}{r} {\scriptstyle 6}\quad{\scriptstyle 18}\;\;{\scriptstyle 1} \\ 7\;.\;\cancel{9}\;0 \\ -5\;.\;9\;8 \\ \hline 1\;.\;9\;2 \end{array}$$

c
$$\begin{array}{r} {\scriptstyle 3}\;\;{\scriptstyle 9}\;\;{\scriptstyle 9}\;\;{\scriptstyle 1} \\ \cancel{4}\;\cancel{0}\;\cancel{0}\;5 \\ -1\;3\;4\;8 \\ \hline 2\;6\;5\;7 \end{array}$$

d
$$\begin{array}{r} {\scriptstyle 1}\;{\scriptstyle 1}\quad{\scriptstyle 4}\;\;{\scriptstyle 15}\;\;{\scriptstyle 1} \\ \cancel{2}\;0\;.\;\cancel{5}\;\cancel{6}\;0 \\ -1\;3\;.\;3\;8\;7 \\ \hline 7\;.\;1\;7\;3 \end{array}$$

2 a
$$\begin{array}{r} 3\;5\;7 \\ \times\quad 4\;6 \\ \hline 2\;1\;4\;2 \\ {\scriptstyle 3}\;{\scriptstyle 4}\quad \\ 1\;4\;2\;8\;0 \\ {\scriptstyle 2}\;{\scriptstyle 2}\quad\quad \\ \hline 1\;6\;4\;2\;2 \\ \hline {\scriptstyle 1}\quad\quad \end{array}$$

b
$$2\overline{)1\;7\;{}^{1}2}\quad\begin{array}{c}8\;6\end{array}$$

c
$$7\overline{)7\;\cancel{2}\;{}^{2}1}\quad\begin{array}{c}1\;0\;3\end{array}$$

ANSWERS

N4
Box A
1 a 67; 197; 201; 237; 307
  b 45, 96, 99, 100, 166, 286
  c $58 - 28 \rightarrow 30 - 1 \rightarrow 29$
  d $125 - 80 \rightarrow 45 - 5 \rightarrow 40 - 2 \rightarrow 38$
  e $156 \times 50 \rightarrow 78 \times 100 = 7800$
  f $50 \times 70 \rightarrow 5 \times 7$ and $00 \rightarrow 3500 - 70 \rightarrow 3430$
  g 31.2 **h** $4 \times 25 = 100$, so $7 \times 4 \rightarrow 28$

N5
Box A
1 a 468 divides by 2, 3, 6, 9
  b 855 divides by 3, 5, 9
  c 946 divides by 2
  d 19 921 362 divides by 2, 3, 6

2 a 1, 2, 3, 5, 6, 10, 15, 30
  b 1, 2, 3, 4, 6, 9, 12, 18, 36
  c 1, 2, 4, 8, 16, 32, 64
  d 1, 2, 3, 4, 6, 8, 12, 16, 24, 32, 48, 64, 96, 192
  e 1, 2, 3, 4, 5, 6, 8, 9, 10, 12, 15, 18, 20, 24, 30, 36, 40, 45, 60, 72, 90, 120, 180, 360

3 a $2 \times 3 \times 5$
  b $2 \times 2 \times 3 \times 3$
  c $2 \times 2 \times 2 \times 2 \times 2 \times 2$
  d $2 \times 2 \times 2 \times 2 \times 2 \times 2 \times 3$
  e $2 \times 2 \times 2 \times 3 \times 3 \times 5$

N6
Box A
1 a subtracting 4   **b** adding 3
  c doubling   **d** finding a third of (dividing by 3)
  e subtracting from 8   **f** dividing into 9

2 3

N7
Box A
1 Allow at least five hours on ordinary roads; three hours if mainly motorway, plus an hour or so for unexpected hold-ups, so 0800 to 1000.

2 A bath would be perhaps 25 to 30 gallons (around 120 litres); saving on 313 days is about 8000 to 9000 gallons (38 000 to 40 000 litres).

3 a $600 \div 30 = 20$
  b $400 \div 80 \times 300 = 5 \times 300 = 1500$

4 23 (You must round up to the next whole coach.)

Box B
1 You probably need to key $\boxed{\text{MODE}}\ \boxed{\text{FIX}}\ \boxed{3}$.

2 a 143   **b** 1.41   **c** 3.14   **d** 4 320 000   **e** 0.0143

3 69.125 kg to 68.875 kg

4 a 0.2 mm
  b Only 97.5 mm can be accepted (97.4 mm could be rounded down to 97.35 mm, which is not within the tolerance allowed.)

N8
Box A
1 **a** If Liam has one cat, both Karen and Sean have three. If Liam has no
   cats, Sean has the most. Otherwise Karen has the most.
   b 4

2 **a** £3570   **b** £875.50

3 $4000 \div 825 \rightarrow 4$ bars per length, so 3 lengths are needed.

4 90

N9
Box A
1 $-1, -0.56, -0.5, -0.4, -0.101, -0.08, 0.1$

2 **a** -4 **b** -2 **c** 2   **d** 2   **e** 3
  f 3   **g** 3   **h** 1   **i** -2 **j** 2

N10
Box A
1 $\frac{5}{9}$

2 $\frac{4}{15}$

3 **a** 18   **b** 14   **c** 27

4 288

5 **A** £300; **B** £350; **C** £400; **D** £450; **E** £550; **F** £650; **G** £750; **H** £900

Box B
1 **a** 0.6   **b** 0.04   **c** $0.\dot{7}$ **d** $0.\dot{2}\dot{7}$

2 **a** $\frac{7}{100}$ **b** $\frac{3}{20}$ **c** $\frac{3}{1000}$ **d** $\frac{2}{125}$

3 **a** $\frac{3}{10}$ **b** $\frac{1}{3}$ **c** $\frac{1}{9}$ **d** $\frac{35}{99}$ **e** $\frac{44}{333}$

4 **a** $\frac{3}{20}, \frac{3}{10}, \frac{3}{8}, \frac{3}{7}$
  b $\frac{4}{11}, \frac{1}{2}, \frac{5}{8}, \frac{99}{100}$

N11
Box A
1 **a** $2\frac{14}{15}$ **b** $10\frac{7}{18}$ **c** $3\frac{13}{24}$ **d** $1\frac{5}{17}$
  e $4\frac{7}{15}$ **f** $6\frac{1}{2}$ **g** $2\frac{1}{30}$ **h** $\frac{5}{6}$

N12
Box A
1 **a** 0.48   **b** 0.07   **c** 0.1225   **d** 0.0675

2 105.8 m

3 20%

4 40%

5 8.6%

6 £118.125 m or £118 125 000

7 £1 036 000

8 Error = 5 miles; True = 80 miles; Error = 6.25%

Box B

1 a £231.78 **b** £302.26

N13
Box A
1 55 g

2 42

3 1:2 500 000

4 a 937 **b** 2437:1500

N14
Box A
1 53

2 £19.20 each

3 a £41.13 **b** £14.57 **c** £270.25 **d** £80.78 **e** £96.88
   f £1092.75

4 (6 · 7 ÷ 7) ÷ (4 · 5 × 4 · 9) =

5 4 · 5 × 4 · 9 = STO 6 · 7 ÷ 7 = ÷ RM =

Box B
1 e.g. 2·5 → 39·. .; 2·25 → 25·. .; 2·15 → 21·. .;
   2·1 → 19·. .; 2·12 → 20·. .; 2·11 → 19·. .;
   2·115 → 20·00. .; 2·1145 → 19·99; so 2·115 to 3 dp
   The test of 2·1145 was necessary to see if 2·114 or 2·115 was nearer.

2 a 42.95 **b** 0.7579

3 0.000 055 769 547 We did it with 19 presses – remember you can type
   ·605, and in this case only need = once and one bracket at the start of
   the bottom numbers.
   = closes all brackets, so) is not needed before = .

N15
Box A
1 New York 7.32×10^6 London 6.68×10^6
   India 8.44×10^8 Monaco 2.47×10^4

2 5×10^{-2}; 3×10^{-2} and 7.5×10^{-2}; 7×10^{-3}

3 a 7.26×10^1 **b** 4.00×10^{-3} **c** 3.35×10^{-1} **d** 1.78×10^6

4 They would have 720 cm² each. Yes, it is possible with a squash!

N16
Box A
1 a B

For **b** and **c** see Figure NA16:1.

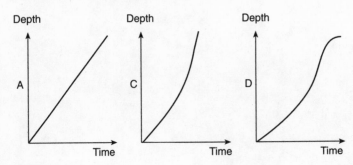

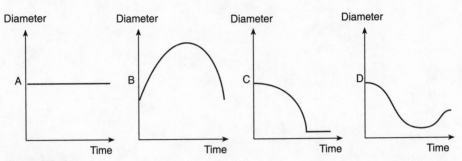

Figure NA16:1

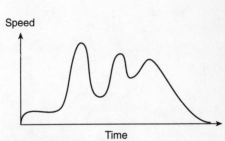

Figure NA16:2

2 a C to E

b See Figure NA16:2.

3 See Figure NA16:3.

4 Toby left Bangor at 8 a.m. and walked 16 miles at an average speed of just over 4 miles per hour without stopping.

Ella set out for Bangor at 8:45 a.m., reaching there at 9 a.m., an average speed of 64 mph. She passed Toby at about 8:55 when they were 4 miles from Bangor. She stopped in Bangor for $1\frac{1}{2}$ hours, leaving at 10:30 a.m. and reached her starting point at 11 a.m, averaging 32 miles per hour. She drove past Toby at about 10:50 a.m. when they were 12 miles from Bangor.

5 Horizontal scale not given; vertical scale jumps from 0 to 100 then steps of 10, thus exaggerating the effect. It does not say what is being sold and is obviously not based on any factual data. Altogether a very good example of a very unmathematical graph!

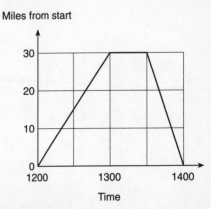

Figure NA16:3

Algebra

A1
Box A
1 a 15	**b** 1	**c** 1	**d** 30	**e** 18
f 50	**g** 5	**h** −1	**i** −3	**j** 50

Box B
1 £18

2 0.8375 N

Box C
1 a 86°F   **b** −40°F (the only time they are the same)

2 a 81   **b** 32   **c** 49   **d** 7   **e** −4 and −0.5

3 −3 and 1

A2

Box A

1 a $2a+5$ **b** $4-a$ **c** 14 **d** $1-e$ **e** $8er-8e+2$ **f** ag

2 a $4a^2f$ **b** $12g^3h$ **c** $6a^5c^2d$ **d** $40e^4f^2g$

3 a 2 **b** $2a$ **c** $3a^2b$ **d** $\dfrac{1}{2yz}$

Box B

1 a $4s-8t$ **b** $4-5w+15e$ **c** $a-ab-ac$

2 a $5a-a^2$ **b** $2a+a^2$ **c** $5-4a+16e$ **d** $2a^2-a$

3 a $x^2-8x+15$ **b** x^2+6x-7 **c** e^2-f^2 **d** $4a^2-9b^2$

Box C

a $3(x+2)$ **b** $a(b-c)$ **c** $2a(b+2a)$ **d** $3ab(a-1)$ **e** $\pi r(2r+l)$
f $2\pi r(r+h)$

Box D

1 a $x=\dfrac{a+2gh}{3}$ **b** $g=\dfrac{3x-a}{2h}$

2 $s=\dfrac{x-v-3t}{3}$

3 $r=\sqrt[3]{\dfrac{3V}{4\pi}}$

4 $g=\dfrac{4\pi^2 l}{t^2}$

A3

Box A

1 a 2 **b** 0 **c** -2 **d** -2.5 **e** $-6\frac{1}{3}$

2 a 6 **b** -3 **c** 8 **d** -4 **e** 9 **f** 3 **g** 1

Box B

1 a $2, 3$ **b** $-1, 1.5$ **c** $-\frac{1}{3}, -1\frac{1}{2}$

2 $0, 2$

3 $-1.37, 4.37$

Box C

1 a $x=3, y=1$ **b** $x=2, y=0$
  c $a=2, b=-1$ **d** $e=-1, f=3$

2 a $x=3, y=-1$ **b** $x=-2, y=3$
  c $c=2, d=-1$ **d** $g=-\frac{1}{3}, h=-2$

A4

Box A

1 a Add 2; 12
  b Add one more than you added last time; 28
  c Square the next counting number; 36
  d Cube the next counting number; 216
  e Subtract half the number you subtracted last time; 1.125

  f Reciprocal $\left(\dfrac{1}{x}\right)$ of the next multiple of 7, $\frac{1}{42}$

2 a $1, 4, 7, 10, 13$ **b** $1, 3, 6, 10, 15$
  c $1, 10, 100, 1000, 10\,000$ (Note n^0 is 1 for all values of n)

3 a $2n+5$ **b** $20-3n$ **c** n^2+n+1 or $n(n+1)+1$

A5
Box A
1 7, 6, 5, 4, 3, 2, 1

2 See Figure AA5:1.

3 See Figure AA5:2.

Box B
1 See Figure AA5:3.

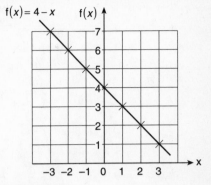

Figure AA5:1

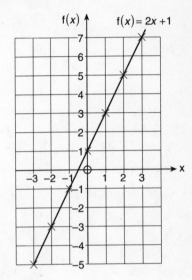

Figure AA5:2

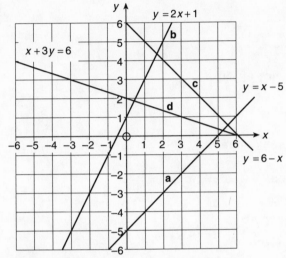

Figure AA5:3

2 $y = -x + 4$

3 a (0,0); 3   **b** (0,7); −4

4 a 2   **b** $-\frac{1}{3}$

A6
Box A
1 a $16 < n < 18$ **b** $65 > w \geqslant 21$ **c** $16 \geqslant p \geqslant 5$

2 a $x > 7$ **b** $x < 3$ **c** $x \geqslant 5$ **d** $x \leqslant -1$

3 See Figure AA6:1.

4 See Figure AA6:2.

Shape

S1
Box A
1 a (i) 45°, **(ii)** 135°, **(iii)** 45°
  b (i) obtuse, **(ii)** acute
  c (i) any of a and b, b and c, c and d, d and a, e and f, f and g, g and h, h and e
    (ii) c and f, d and e (a and h and b and g are not alternate, but they are equal)
    (iii) any of a and c, b and d, e and g, f and h
    (iv) any of a and f, b and e, c and h, d and g
    (v) c and e, d and f

2 240°, 270°, 330°

3 13.2 cm, 10.3 cm; 3.9 cm, 1.9 cm; 6.4 cm, 2.4 cm

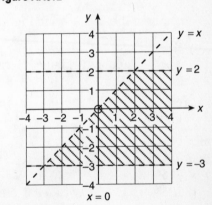

Figure AA6:1

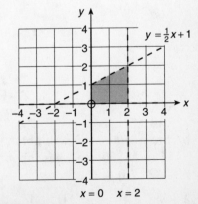

Figure AA6:2

Box B

1 a cube   **b** square-based pyramid   **c** cone
   d cylinder   **e** triangular prism
   f tetrahedron   **g** triangular prism

S2
Box A

1 c is impossible

2 equilateral (equal-sided)

3 a square   **b** circle

4 18°

5 d Exterior would be 108°, which is not a factor of 360°.

6 Exterior $= \frac{2}{15} \times 180° = 24°$
   Sides $= 360 \div 24 = 15$

7 a e.g. four sides; one pair of parallel sides; angle sum 360°
   b two equal sides; equal diagonals
   Note: Both could have two equal angles, if they were 90° in the non-
        isosceles one.

8 kite, parallelogram, rectangle

9 kite, rhombus, square

S3
Box A

1

Shape	a	b	c	d	e	f	g	h	i	j
(i) Lines	1	3	1	0	1	0	2	2	4	6
(ii) Rotational order	1	3	1	1	1	2	2	2	4	6

2 One possibility is shown in Figure SA3:1.

Box B

1

Shape	cuboid	cube	tetra	□-pyr	△-prism
Planes	3	9	6	4	4
Axes	3	13	7	1	4
Sym. No.	4	24	12	4	6

Figure SA3:1

S4
Box A

1 a 315°   **b** SE   **c** W   **d** 225°   **e** 015°
   f 205°   **g** S10°W   **h** N60°W   **i** S85°W

2 A, 055°; B, 262°

3 310°; 6.4 km

S5
Box A
No answers.

S6
Box A

1 a A to A2; x-axis
   b A to A2; 90° clockwise about the origin
     A1 to A2; 90° clockwise about (4.5, 0.5)
   c (i) 2   **(ii)** $\frac{1}{2}$
   d right 5, down 4 or $\begin{pmatrix} 5 \\ -4 \end{pmatrix}$

2 See Figure SA6:1.

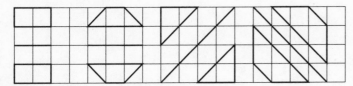

Figure SA6:1

3 See Figure SA6:2.

a

d

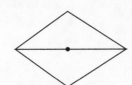

g

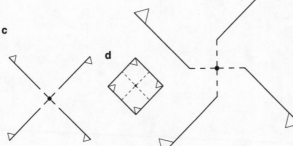

Figure SA6:2

4 See Figure SA6:3.

a

b

c

d

e

Figure SA6:3

5 a right 6, up 3 or $\begin{pmatrix} 6 \\ 3 \end{pmatrix}$ **b** left 6, down 3 or $\begin{pmatrix} -6 \\ -3 \end{pmatrix}$

c left 4, up 1 or $\begin{pmatrix} -4 \\ 1 \end{pmatrix}$ **d** right 4, down 1 or $\begin{pmatrix} 4 \\ -1 \end{pmatrix}$

6

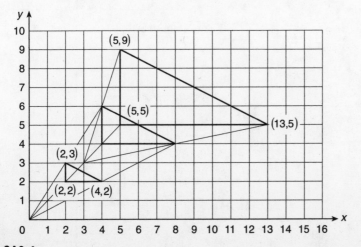

Figure SA6:4

e (5,9), (5,5), (13,5); (2,2), (4,2), (2,3)

7 See Figure SA6:5.

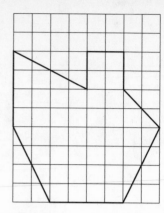

Figure SA6:5

S7
Box A
1 B

2 CK; DL; FI

3 B and C (Tetrahedrons do not have to have equilateral triangles.)

4 b and c

5 Scale factor is 4:5; AC = 7.2 cm; XY = 6.3 cm

6 a 5:3   **b** 3:2

S8
Box A
1 See Figure SA8:1.

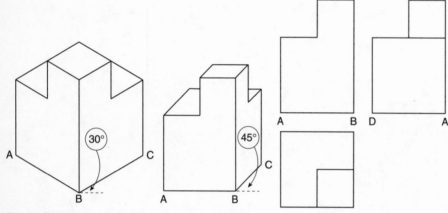

Figure SA8:1

2 See Figure SA8:2.

3 See Figure SA8:3.

4 See Figure SA8:4.

S9
Box A
1 a isosceles triangle   **b** rhombus

Measure

M1
Box A
1 a 0.0245 km   **b** 50 mg   **c** 15 400 mm
   d 0.05 litres   **e** 2.005 kg   **f** 0.1089 m

Box B
1 a 1535   **b** 1h 28 min   **c** 1338 (change at Exeter)
   d The 1035 takes just over two hours, about 84 mph.

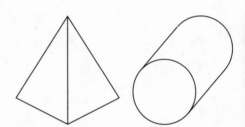

Figure SA8:2

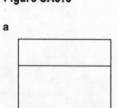

Figure SA8:3

a

b

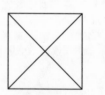

c

Figure SA8:4

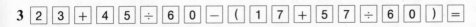

2 The calculator subtracts the 4 hours but adds the 37 min so it does $8 + \frac{25}{60} - 4 + \frac{37}{60}$. To correct it, use brackets around the 4 hours 27 minutes, but remember 3.8 is 3 hours $+ \frac{8}{10}$ of an hour $= 3$ hours 48 min. You could also change it all to minutes first, or use the degree/minute/second key.

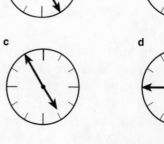

3 $\boxed{2}\ \boxed{3}\ \boxed{+}\ \boxed{4}\ \boxed{5}\ \boxed{\div}\ \boxed{6}\ \boxed{0}\ \boxed{-}\ \boxed{(}\ \boxed{1}\ \boxed{7}\ \boxed{+}\ \boxed{5}\ \boxed{7}\ \boxed{\div}\ \boxed{6}\ \boxed{0}\ \boxed{)}\ \boxed{=}$

4 0.0206 seconds; she could run as fast as the runner in lane one but lose by 0.02 seconds. Not fair!

M2
Box A
1 a (i) 9:10   **(ii)** ten past nine   **(iii)** 0910   **(iv)** 2110
   b (i) 1:25   **(ii)** twenty-five past one   **(iii)** 0125   **(iv)** 1325
   c (i) 4:15   **(ii)** quarter past four   **(iii)** 0415   **(iv)** 1615
   d (i) 12:30   **(ii)** half past twelve   **(iii)** 1230   **(iv)** 0030
   e (i) 5:35   **(ii)** twenty-five to six   **(iii)** 0535   **(iv)** 1735

2 See Figure MA2.

Figure MA2

Box B
1 a 0.1   **b** 0.5   **c** 0.8   **d** 1.25   **e** 1.5   **f** 1.75
   g 2.4   **h** 2.8   **i** 31.75   **j** 32.25   **k** 32.625   **l** 33.125

2 1:51, nearly $\frac{3}{4}$ full, 33 mph/about 53 km/h, 25 336.3 miles, 147.7 miles, about normal temperature, about 35 lb per square inch oil pressure

3 a 2.6 kg   **b** 2.4 kg   **c** 3.8 kg

4 a 360°C   **b** 5.5 s   **c** 9 gallons   **d** 4.6 kg
   e 260 V   **f** 36.8°C

M3
Box A
1 488 m^2

2 a 6.57 m   **b** 2.81 m^2 **c** 65.7 m^2 **d** 28.1 m^3 (28 100 litres)

3 56.74 kg

4 a area   **b** volume   **c** volume   **d** area
   e impossible   **f** length   **g** impossible

5 The one with length × length (r^2) must be for area.

M4
Box A
1 a 72.0 m   **b** 5.58 cm   **c** 13.0 cm   **d** 11.0 m

Box B
1 77 m

2 a 11.5 cm^2 **b** 69 cm^3 **c** 58.5 cm

3 a 115.6 cm; 457.5 cm^2 **b** 0.228 m^3

M5
Box A
1 a 2.66   **b** 5.49   **c** 56.3°   **d** 31°   **e** 1.46

Box B
1 a 4.66   **b** 4.23   **c** 26.6°   **d** 30°   **e** 8.39   **f** 6.43

2 See Figure MA5:1.
 a 76 km north, 33 km west (Use two right-angled triangles.)
 b 337°, 83 km (Use answers to **a**.)

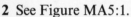

Figure MA5:1

Data handling

D1
Box A

1 Strata should be all five areas (perhaps in proportion to the number of workers in each), sex (again, perhaps in proportion), age of service in classes (less than 1 year, 1 to 5 years etc.). Random selection within these, perhaps by work-code reference numbers. She should aim to sample up to 10% to have a good chance of a reliable report.

2 Possible answers are:
 a Will get long answers; very difficult to process.
 b Biased; people are likely to say what the questioner seems to want them to say.
 c Will get long answers; biased towards only thinking of benefits.
 d People will not know what you are talking about, nor how to reply. Answers may well not be about the planned changes at all.
 e Good; sets out what is to happen and offers unbiased choices. Could be improved by adding 'strongly agree/agree' etc.
 f Provocative; people might well object to being told they live in a slum! Biased towards local management, and many people might not understand what was meant by that.
 g Too much all at once. Most of it is not relevant, an infringement of privacy and very likely to cause offence. The only question that could be connected with the survey is imprecise and will not yield useful data.

D2
Box A

1		
0–9	~~HH~~ ~~HH~~	10
10–19	~~HH~~ ~~HH~~ ~~HH~~ ~~HH~~ ///	23
20–29	~~HH~~ ~~HH~~ ~~HH~~ ~~HH~~ ~~HH~~ ~~HH~~ ~~HH~~ ///	38
30–39	~~HH~~ ~~HH~~ ~~HH~~ ~~HH~~	20
40–49	~~HH~~ ////	9

2 a 10–15: 15.3; nearer to 15 than 16
   16–20: 15.8; nearer to 16 than 15
 b 131–140: 135, 140; within class range
   141–150: 142; within class range
 c under 17: none; all are 17 or more
   17–21: 17 y 3 m; within class range; 21 y 10 m; not yet 22
   22–25: none; all are under 22 or over 25
   over 25: 25 y 2 m; within class range

D3
Box A
1 See Figures DA3:1–6.

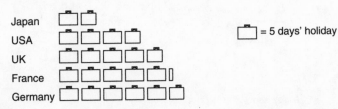

Figure DA3:1

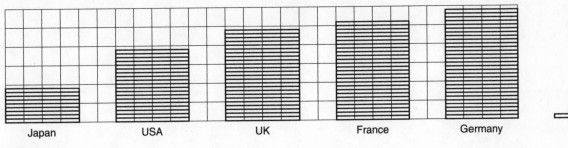

Figure DA3:2

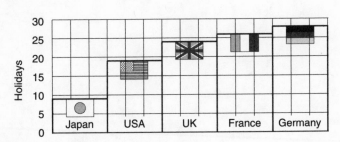

Figure DA3:3

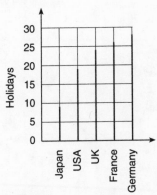

Figure DA3:4

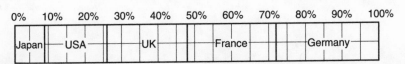

Figure DA3:5

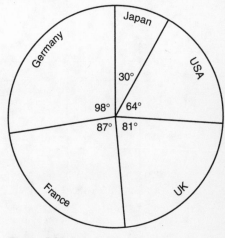

Figure DA3:6

2 See Figure DA3:7.

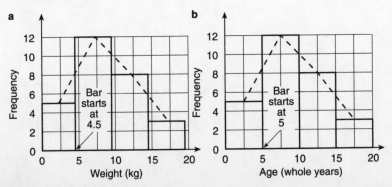

Figure DA3:7

Box B

1 See Figure DA3:8.

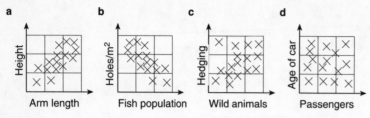

Figure DA3:8

2 See the three graphs in Figure DA3:9.

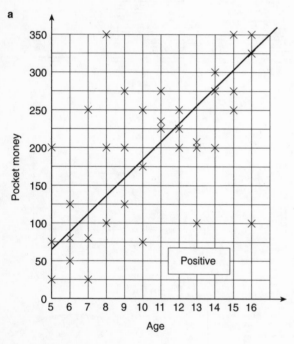

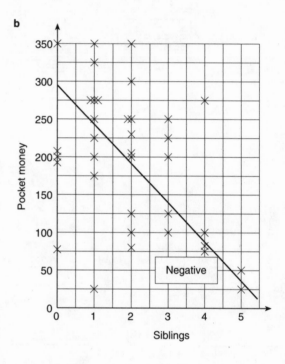

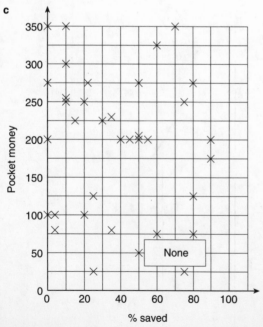

Figure DA3:9

Box C

| 1 | 3 | 10 | 18 | 29 | 41 | 48 | 53 |

and see Figure DA3:10.

2 Most women's pay is between £100 and £300.
Men's pay is more spread out, with close to the same numbers of men receiving £200, £300, £400 and £500. (If it were the same number the line would be straight.)
Only half of the men but nearly all of the women earn under £300.

D4
Box A

1 a Mode, 5; median, 5; mean, 5.06; range, 8 (9 minus 1)
IQ-range, 2 (6 minus 4)
  b Mode, 3 litres; median, 3 litres;
mean, 3.21 litres; range, 5 litres;
IQ-range, 2 litres ($4-2$)
  c Mode, 0 occupants; median, 5 occupants;
mean, 4.26 occupants; range, 8 occupants;
IQ-range, 6 occupants ($7-1$)

2 See Figure DA4.

Box B

1 a As the data is fairly normal the measures represent it well.
  b As part **a**
  c Data is not normal, in fact very much the opposite, and knowing all the measures clearly shows this. One measure on its own would be very misleading though.

2 a No pupil truants for more than one day.
  b The total absences counted as truanting divided by the number of pupils in the school is less than one (but this could, for example, be three pupils truanting for 50 days and 148 never truanting).
  c All pupils truant for one day a year.
Other answers are possible.

3 a Everyone has the same score.
  b For example 24 score 30, 1 scores 5, average (mean) is 29.

4 Probably that the mode is about £190; that is, more people earn something near to £190 than any other wage. It cannot be accurate as wages are not fixed; it could be a mean based on annual income tax returns, though this would not pick up all earnings. It could be an estimate found by taking a random sample.

5 People often assume the data is normal, when all averages *are* in the middle.

D5
Box A

1 Possible answers could be:
  a very likely/almost certainly
  b very unlikely (unless they are sun-glasses)
  c very likely/almost certainly
  d impossible under the present constitution
  e about evens
  f less than evens/quite unlikely (There are seven possible coins.)

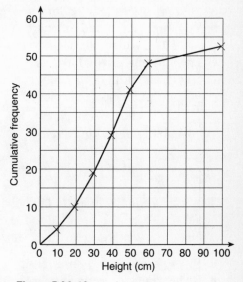

Figure DA3:10

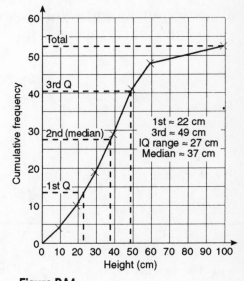

1st ≈ 22 cm
3rd ≈ 49 cm
IQ range ≈ 27 cm
Median ≈ 37 cm

Figure DA4

2 a There is at least one red or one green bead.

  b You might soon find there are at least two colours. After a lot of picks (say 50+) you might begin to think there are *only* two colours.

  c The more picks you have recorded, the more you should be able to predict the ratio of the colours e.g. twice as many red as green. The fraction $\dfrac{\text{number of reds picked}}{\text{number of picks}}$ will get closer and closer to the true probability of picking a red.

Box B

1 $\frac{10}{1000}$ or $\frac{1}{100}$ or 1% or 0.01

2 The coin is equally likely to fall heads or tails, but the chance of winning could not be said to be equal to the chance of drawing. It depends on ability, how well they play, luck, etc.

3 a 13 **b** $\frac{13}{20}$ **c** $\frac{7}{14}$ or evens

  d By hearing six wrong answers he may have realised why his original answer is wrong and had second thoughts.

4 a BBBB, BBBG, BBGB, BBGG, BGBB, BGBG, BGGB, BGGG
    GBBB, GBBG, GBGB, GBGG, GGBB, GGBG, GGGB, GGGG

  b $\frac{1}{16}$; $\frac{6}{16}$ or $\frac{3}{8}$

5 0.35

D6

Box A

1 a $\frac{1}{2} \times \frac{1}{2} = \frac{1}{4}$

  b $\frac{1}{4}$

  c $\frac{4}{5} \times \frac{4}{5} = \frac{16}{25}$

  d $\frac{1}{2} \times \frac{3}{10} + \frac{3}{10} \times \frac{1}{2} = \frac{3}{10}$

  e $\frac{1}{5} \times \frac{4}{5} + \frac{4}{5} \times \frac{1}{5} = \frac{8}{25}$

2 a (i) 0.12   **(ii)** $0.7 \times 0.4 = 0.28$
      (iii) $0.3 \times 0.6 = 0.18$ **(iv)** $0.7 \times 0.6 = 0.42$

  b The sum should be 1 as all possibilities have been covered.

  c 25 kg should give $25 \times 0.42 = 10.5$ kg of acceptable carrots. Five boxes will probably be needed.

3

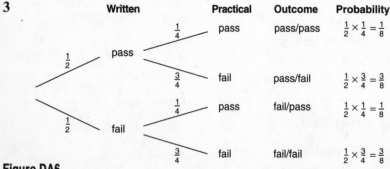

Figure DA6

4 Not every contestant will get the same score; some will be better at the quiz than others, so it is not an equal chance situation.

5 a A random pupil is equally likely to be in each of the ten sets.

  b Knowing the pupil is in Set 1 for one subject increases the probability that the same pupil is in Set 1 for the other subject.

6 $\frac{29}{32}$